# Sex, Diet and Tanning

## The curious story of the drug to induce a natural tan including all you ever wanted to know about tanning

by Terence Winters, PhD
and Robert Dorr, PhD

The contents of this work, including, but not limited to, the accuracy of events, people, and places depicted; opinions expressed; permission to use previously published materials included; and any advice given or actions advocated are solely the responsibility of the author, who assumes all liability for said work and indemnifies the publisher against any claims stemming from publication of the work.

All Rights Reserved
Copyright © 2021 by Terence Winters, PhD, and Robert Dorr, PhD

No part of this book may be reproduced or transmitted, downloaded, distributed, reverse engineered, or stored in or introduced into any information storage and retrieval system, in any form or by any means, including photocopying and recording, whether electronic or mechanical, now known or hereinafter invented without permission in writing from the publisher.

Dorrance Publishing Co
585 Alpha Drive
Pittsburgh, PA 15238
Visit our website at *www.dorrancebookstore.com*

ISBN: 978-1-6386-7115-2
eISBN: 978-1-6386-7932-5

Dedicated to the memory of Dr. Mac Hadley, one of the founders of the company and a fine human being.

This book, in two parts, is a joint effort of Bob Dorr and Terry Winters, who worked together since 1993 to try to develop a commercial product out of one of the molecules found to induce natural tanning without sunlight based on work done at the University of Arizona in Tucson. The authors have shared writing the chapters and have indicated in the heading of each chapter who is relating the story. The story in this book goes from the creation of the product in the late 1980s through to 2007, when we were no longer associated with the company. At that time, the drug was well on its way to becoming a commercial product and has since been approved for an orphan indication in the EU, in 2015, and the USA, in 2019. Hopefully, the management at Clinuvel can complete the story from 2007 onwards.

Explaining the science is a key part of the story, but to make it easy for the general, non-scientific reader, the first part tells the business part of the story, and we have put together Bob's lucid chapters on the science in the second part, which can be read separately depending on your appetite for the chemical and biological sciences.

Although Bob and Terry got to write the story, the real heroes are the scientists and physicians at the University of Arizona, from around the world, who worked for many years trying to unravel the fascinating biological story of how humans tan and then set out to try to mimic that process with a safe and efficacious drug. In the process. they found a new family of biological pathways that could be influenced by variations of this drug to control sexual arousal and appetite, among other things. Unique drugs based on this family are now on, or close to, the market for all three of these natural processes, and there are probably many different indications still to be developed based on what are now known as the melanocortins.

All of this cutting-edge science was made possible by the US government through the NIH, or National Institutes of Health, which provided the grants for the university's research and is the main reason why the United States leads the world in development of new drugs, as described in chapter three. For this, we are grateful.

# Contents

# Prologue

Arizona lies between California and New Mexico on the United States' southern border with Mexico and is one of the sunniest places in the world. Southern Arizona, where Tucson is located, gets about 330 days of sunshine per year. Since this area was settled mainly by white Europeans, it should come as no surprise that it is also one of the four "world hotspots" for the high incidence of skin cancer and other human ailments caused by excessive sun exposure.

The other three "hotspots" are Australia, Scandinavia, and Scotland. Australia is included for the same reason as Arizona with the additional bonus of having more intense sun since it is closer to the equator. However, the reason for Scandinavia and Scotland being in this unfortunate group is that although neither place gets much sunshine, when the sun does shine, the people, mostly European blue-eyed blondes, redheads, and other white people with minimal sun resistance, celebrate by throwing caution to the winds, stripping off, and exposing the maximum parts of their bodies to the sun for the longest possible time. So, they frequently end up with horrendous sunburns, which are the main cause of skin cancer and related problems later in life.

Skin cancer is the most prevalent form of cancer with the incidence approximately equal to the sum of all other cancers. Yes, that's right, the incidence of skin cancer is the same as all other cancers combined. Dermatologists in Arizona are very busy, and it can take months for a patient to get an appointment. Therefore, the University of Arizona Medical Center in Tucson has for decades been the recipient of one of the largest grants from the National Institutes of Health (NIH) to study the effects of sun exposure on the human body. The university also has some outstanding physicians and scientists to pursue these studies.

One of the fascinating areas that they have been researching for a long time is the biochemistry and mechanism of action of how sun exposure causes human skin to develop a tan. This led them into a study of the pigment-producing cells of the skin called melanocytes and how these cells produce the substance known as melanin, which is the dark pigment responsible for natural tanning. Sun-damaged melanocytes are also responsible for the deadliest form of skin cancer, known as melanoma, and can also be responsible, by their absence, for "Michael Jackson disease," or vitiligo, which shows up as irregular nonpigmented skin patches in various places and can be seriously disfiguring all over the body. The university researchers' obvious goal was to control tanning, but without sunlight, in order to confer skin cancer protection. That is because it has been known for a long time that the incidence of skin cancer decreases dramatically as skin pigmentation increases. In other words, dark-skinned people get almost no skin cancers, and light-skinned, blond, and freckled people get a lot of it. Melanin pigment is the reason why darker skins are protected.

The team in Tucson studied the hormone known as melanocyte stimulating hormone, or α-MSH, which was known to be produced after sun exposure and to cause the melanocytes to acquire melanin and, thereby, a natural tan in the exposed parts of the skin.

We need to digress for a moment to explain the chemical basis of α-MSH, which is a peptide made by combining together amino acids which are essential for life. There are twenty-three natural amino acids, and they can combine together to form up to about a thousand-unit chains. Up to about one hundred amino acids linked together are called peptides, and greater than one hundred, they are proteins. Peptides and proteins are made naturally by our cells and are very active in most biological functions. You may have heard of some amino acids, such as glycine, tryptophan, and alanine, and possibly of some peptides, such as insulin, used to treat diabetics, and Lupron for prostate cancer. α-MSH is a thirteen-amino acid chain peptide. Each amino acid exists in two forms known as stereoisomers, or mirror images that are related in the same way as your right and left hands, identical but not superimposable—try superimposing your hands and you will see what we mean. All-natural peptides and proteins are made from the levo (left) or L-forms of amino acids, but chemists can use the dextro (right) D-forms to create some interesting properties, as we shall see.

It would have been nice if α-MSH could have been isolated and used directly as a drug, but it is very unstable in the bloodstream and only acts locally, which is why a tan only forms in those areas which have been directly exposed to the sun. Thus, natural α-MSH is degraded rapidly once formed and is not carried throughout the body in the blood. To overcome these drawbacks, the team began to make synthetic analogs of α-MSH including substituting some of the L-amino acids with the D-forms. This required expert peptide synthetic chemists, and the team in Tucson was fortunate to be led by Dr. Victor Hruby, a world-class peptide chemist with multiple awards from all the prestigious societies.

After they had synthesized these new drug candidates, they had to be purified and then tested to determine their activity in humans. This is where the fun started and resulted in molecules having dramatic effects in totally unexpected areas of human biology, in addition to tanning. The class of molecules became known as the melanocortins. We will give you a peek at some of their activities here, but please read on to get some of the fascinating details. In summary, in addition to their tanning, some of these peptides were found, by a highly amusing accident, to stimulate sexual activity and were also found to control appetite and thereby induce weight loss. Some of the peptides were active in all three areas and were quickly hailed as wonder drugs. However, these particular peptides also have other side effects, and so, development was focused on peptides that had only one specific function. All three of these activities are being separately developed, but this book focuses primarily on the development of the drug to induce a natural tan.

# PART 1
# The Melanotan Story

## The tortuous path to market of the sun-protective tanning drug

Part one tells the story from the creation of the tanning drug in the laboratories of the University of Arizona in Tucson in the late 1980s up to the point in 2007 when we ceased to be involved. At that point, clinical trials were underway to seek approval in the European Union (EU) to treat a rare, serious skin condition. The drug family was first known as the "Melanotans," and the two lead molecules that we focused on were Melanotan-1, or MT-1, which was specific for tanning, and Melanotan-2, or MT-2, which was a truncated form that had activity in tanning and other areas for reasons that will be explained later. Melanotan-1 was also known by its more correct name, afamelanotide, and later, in about 2012, when Melanotan-1 looked like it was going to get to market, it was christened with the trade name "Scenesse."

# Chapter 1

## *From Tucson to Melbourne*

*This is Terry to tell you about some of the highlights of how we got from Tucson to Australia. As you will read, it was not planned!*

This is an international story centered in the USA, Europe, and Australia and highlights the entrepreneurial passion of all who were involved. It includes humor and tragedy, some of which, if found in a novel, would be derided as not credible. However, all the events described herein are true—they really happened, and the result is a safe and effective drug that has helped and will eventually help a lot of people with the treatment and prevention of many serious skin diseases.

Although the key paper on tanning was published by the Tucson scientists in the prestigious Journal of the American Medical Association in 1991, let's begin the story about thirteen years after the experimental drug was first synthesized in Tucson, then we will go back to fill in the gaps and forward to the first approval.

In December 2003, the phone rang in my home office in Scottsdale, Arizona. It was Dr. Wayne Millen, the CEO of Epitan, calling from Melbourne, Australia. I was apprehensive, since I was expecting Wayne to tell me the results of our latest effort to optimize the administration of our tanning drug, being delivered as a controlled release implant under the skin, in the first Australian human clinical trials. This was crunch time, make or break.

"Terry, I have got news for you. You know those white Australians that received the controlled-release implant of Melanotan?"

"Yes, of course. What happened?" I tried to control my nervous expectation.

"Well, we have changed those white Australians into Paul Robesons and Eartha Kitts after about ten days (this is a reference to two dark-skinned singers). They were so delighted with their whole-body tans that they tried them out in our fierce Australian sun. Now they are so dark that they are worried. Cobber, it looks like there is a synergistic effect with sunlight. We have a real winner on our hands! But no one has won the board of directors' guessing game of the best concentration of the drug in the slow-release implant, because it worked with the very lowest drug concentration, and nobody guessed anywhere near it. It is incredible that it is effective at such a low level. Tweaking those melanin receptors continuously at a very low level is so much more effective than the single daily dosages in solution that we had been using."

"Wayne, what about safety and side effects? Did anything show up that concerns you?"

"No, the transient flushing that we had seen with the daily subcutaneous injections did not show up in any of the subjects, and their lab values were normal"

"That is really good news."

I was elated since, in the business of drug development, you don't get too many phone calls like this with such overwhelming good news. Most clinical trials fail, and it is the rare success that keeps us all going. We spent the rest of the phone call talking about the next steps and hurriedly arranging for an in-person board meeting in Melbourne. Epitan Limited was already public on the Australian stock exchange, and the most important thing we had to do, after confirming these clinical results, was to raise more funds to ramp up the development program to a much faster and higher level.

After digesting this news, my first call was to Dr. Robert Dorr, my main contact at the University of Arizona. He was similarly elated since he had been pushing for us to develop a slow release version for a while. He informed the University of Arizona team, and they drew inspiration from this outstanding news.

I am sure that the question has already been raised in your minds of how the drug development got from Tucson to Melbourne, and so I need to digress to explain this long-distance translocation.

In the current prolonged biotechnology stock and financing boom, we quickly forget what it was like when biotech was fighting for its existence in a prolonged investment drought during and after the dot-com era in the 1990s and after the turn of the millennium. At the time, most venture capitalists recoiled from biotech investments like a javelina from a rattlesnake in the Arizona desert. I thought Melanotan was one of the most exciting drug startups that I had yet seen in my venture capital days, but I just could not get any of my VC contemporaries to agree with me. That was despite having a great team of scientist founders in Tucson and Hank Agersborg, the former director of R&D at American Home Products/Wyeth-Ayerst, as the CEO.

But before continuing, we need to introduce your two authors. My name is Terry Winters, and I spent about twenty-five years as a venture capitalist specializing in early-stage seed investing in medical startups out of American universities. This is the most high-risk part of the venture capital business, and you lose more than you win. But it is great fun! I was trained as a chemist in the UK and came to the US in 1967. After a post-doc fellowship at UCLA, I worked for two chemical companies and then lucked into the VC business in 1981, just at the start of the Reagan revolution, a case of good timing. I was a partner with a VC fund in Denver, and we came across Melanotan through our strategy of seeking start-up opportunities at the lesser-known US universities. After all, you trip over the VCs at Stanford, MIT, and other prestigious schools, but the quality of the science is just as good elsewhere.

Bob Dorr, my co-author and trusted friend, has a PhD in medical pharmacology from the University of Arizona after being initially trained as a pharmacist. This makes him an expert in drugs and their actions in the body. He is a founding member of the University of Arizona (UA) Cancer Center and ran their outpatient pharmacy operations for over twenty years. He has over four hundred publications and twenty-seven US patents to his name. He recently retired and is currently Emeritus Professor of Medical Pharmacology at the UA's College of Medicine. In addition, he is a very likeable person and keeps a cool head even when all around are losing theirs. I continue to be impressed by his knowledge and approach to bridging science and business. Without him, the company that you are going to learn about would never have got off the ground.

We founded the start-up US company Melanotan in 1993 and licensed the technology from the University of Arizona in Tucson, AZ. But by 1997, I had exhausted all avenues of fundraising, and my partners would not allow me to add new funds to our Melanotan investment. I had essentially given up on the company and was about to recommend that we write off our $310,000 seed investment when I was contacted by Wayne Millen, my Australian friend whom I met on our postdoctoral chemistry fellowships together at UCLA in California in 1967/8. Wayne had returned to Australia and made a lot of money in the mining analysis business, and we had stayed in touch. He lived in Perth in West Australia, and I visited him a couple of times, after which he became very interested in the venture capital business. So, I invited him to the annual meeting of our Columbine Venture Fund in Vail, Colorado, in 1997 where, among about fifteen other companies, Hank was presenting Melanotan to our fund investors.

Wayne fell in love with the deal and said that if ever we wanted to do something in Australia, this was exactly what investors were looking for since Australia was the skin cancer "capital" of the world, and they would be fascinated with this technology that offers protection from skin cancer without having to be exposed to the sun. Remembering his comments and now at the end of my tether, I called Wayne and asked if he would like to take over and try to get Melanotan financed in Australia. He jumped at the chance, and we did a deal which gave our seed-invested US company, Melanotan, a nice piece of a new company, Epitan, which he formed in Australia. When the deal was done, I promptly forgot about it and went on to my other medical seed investments, never imagining the great saga that was set in motion.

In 2000 I fielded another phone call from Wayne:

"Terry, I got it funded. Went public directly on the ASX (Australian Stock Exchange) and raised seven million Aussie dollars (A$). I'm going to move from Perth to Melbourne to run the company, since that is the center of Australian biotech. There is only one problem, one condition that has to be satisfied. You must join the board of directors."

"No way, Wayne! In fact, NFW! I have got so much going on here in the US that I just can't take a week every quarter to come to Australia for board meetings. My VC partners would never let me do it. And I know nothing about doing business in Australia, so it is a nonstarter, etc. etc."

So that's how it happened that I joined the Epitan board of directors, and a month later, my wife and I were on a plane to Melbourne from Los Angeles for the very first Epitan board meeting. I had cut a deal with Wayne to keep the travel costs reasonable by going economy class but having a suite at the Hyatt in Melbourne for my stay. It was a deal that saved the company a lot of money, and I was able to take my wife with me most times (at our expense!) to combine the board meeting with some sightseeing. This was only fair, because she had been one of the biggest supporters of trying to get this drug to market, and she foresaw an enormous cosmetic market for a tanning drug similar to the huge market for Botox for wrinkles. Look at the number of tanning salons in the US, about 6,500, for a proxy on the size of this potential market. She had a point.

But this trip was the last time we would sit in economy for sixteen non-stop hours, and thereafter, we went through Auckland, New Zealand, which gave us an intermediate stop and made the trip into two legs of twelve and four hours, still in economy but easier to take. Distances are very long in the Antipodes!

So, to quote Winston Churchill, this was the end of the beginning of how we got started with a real public company in Australia. Now we will give you more details of this incredible story, starting with the birth of the molecule in Dr. Victor Hruby's lab in Tucson.

# Chapter 2
## *Melanotan-2 and Mac Hadley*

*This is Bob to tell you about Mac and how his habit of self-testing the drug candidates yielded a surprising result.*

In the spring of 1994, University of Arizona (UA) biology professor Mac Hadley decided to try our newest peptide tanning drug on himself. He didn't tell anyone on the development team, but as the pharmacist for the studies, I suspected something was up when he asked for a supply of powdered drug "for a very large rat." He then cleared his throat on the phone and said he needed the drug for a series of rat studies, and I said, "Fine, I'll weigh it out." My lab was on the fourth floor of the Arizona Cancer Center on the medical campus and next to the University Hospital. Professor Hadley's lab was in the Bio-West Building on the main UA campus, about one mile south of the medical campus. Mac sent one of his graduate students to pick up the drug, which we were calling Melanotan-2 (MT-2), after the precursor molecule Melanotan-1 (MT-1, now afamelanotide). MT-1 was a creation of UA chemist and Regents Professor Victor Hruby's, PhD, graduate student Tomi Sawyer. MT-1 had two chemical modifications from the natural animal pigmentation hormone alpha-melanocyte stimulating hormone (α-MSH). The chemical modifications in MT-1 produced extreme potency in animal pigmentation models.

Mac's work on these models included frogs, lizards, and special "pigmentable" rodents. Professor Hadley was a close collaborator and co-inventor of these new pigmentation molecules wherein his lab handled all of the animal pigmentation studies with these new molecules. This group of molecules is now known as the "melanotropic peptides," since they are comprised of short, thirteen or less, amino acid chains, with their sequence based on the structure of natural α-MSH, which will produce pigmentation.

When Mac asked for the supply of MT-2, we already knew that these short peptides could induce tanning in humans. We documented that in a 1991 publication in the Journal of the American Medical Association. In that publication, we used normal human volunteers, mostly graduate students hungry for some additional money. The subjects were given ten daily subcutaneous, or SQ, injections of the afamelanotide peptide that we were calling Melanotan-1. Prior to that, it was scientific dogma that humans could not respond to pigmentation hormones. The example was the snow hare, whose fur turns brown in the summer and white in the winter in response to an α-MSH signal from a special lobe of the pituitary gland. In contrast, humans were "naked apes" that lacked the ability to change pigmentation from hormones since we did not have the part of the pituitary that was responsible for producing the pigmentation hormone, α-MSH. But in that 1991 publication, we showed that humans *could* respond to an injected derivative (MT-1) of the natural pigmentation hormone, α-MSH. Besides the visible tanning, those first subjects given MT-1 also showed an immediate flushing of the face and upper torso after the injections, and some also reported vague symptoms of nausea without any vomiting or apparent decrease in food intake or weight loss.

Mac Hadley was not your typical university science professor, if there is such an archetype. He'd come up the academic ladder from the humblest of beginnings. Prior to getting an "out of the blue" scholarship to prestigious Brown University, Mac was driving a delivery truck on the East Coast. As a US Navy corpsman in the early 1950s, he'd been sent to special combat training and then assigned to a Marine combat unit in Korea. That unit was involved in the early and most brutal days of the Korean War. He saw lots of trauma, field-treated horrific battle wounds, and was not afraid to use his rifle when no one needed patching up. After his time in Korea, he'd been assigned to corpsman duty in Japan, where US forces maintained a very large presence.

One of the consistent jobs in Japan involved tracking down which brothel a Marine had visited after he'd been diagnosed with a venereal disease. The follow-up procedure was not delicate: a group of Navy Shore Patrol members was assembled, and arriving simultaneously in multiple military vehicles, they would surround the brothel to prevent any escape. Then, Mac and some of the other Navy corpsmen would go in and methodically treat every female present with antibiotics using deep intramuscular injections of concentrated penicillin medications. A man with that experience would have no problem giving himself a simple subcutaneous (SQ) injection.

By the time of his MT-2 self-injection adventure, Mac was in his early sixties with a slight build, a ruddy complexion, and very thinned hair. He also had a way of looking at you sort of out of the side of his eyes. He would slightly squint and give off a subconscious signal that he was somehow sizing you up for a fight. It was similar when he asked a scientific question, which often seemed to imply a bit of contempt in the asking. Part of that may have been his hearing loss, which caused him to speak at an abnormally loud volume. His penchant for starting sentences in the middle of a thought train had also earned him the play-on-words moniker of his name "Hack Madly" by his undergraduate biology students. But while his speech often seemed disjointed, Mac was an eloquent writer, and he produced beautiful first drafts of scientific manuscripts. That is not easy to do, and some scientists never learn it. He was also a successful multiyear author of the premier textbook on nonhuman endocrinology. In short, he was a no-niceties, straight forward, sometimes gruff, and highly competent scientist, with world-class expertise in the biology of pigmentation.

I gave Mac's graduate student the weighed-out MT-2 and didn't think about it again until Mac appeared at my cancer center office unannounced at about 10 A.M. two days after the grad student picked up the drug. He bounded into the office and, pro forma, started his sentence in the middle of a thought: "That drug is phenomenal," Note that at first, I didn't really know which drug he was talking about since I had at least fifty melanotropin peptide analogs in my freezer that both Mac and I had been working on in various animal studies. Plus, Mac had not told anyone he was going to inject himself with MT-2, so I probably had a puzzled look on my face. Mac realized that and slowed down a bit but did not drop his voice, which meant all the secretaries and admins in the outer office pooled-desk area could hear everything.

Mac said he'd injected himself with the MT-2 I had provided. He gave himself a subcutaneous injection at mid-morning of the day after the student had picked up the powder. He said he'd felt warm-faced immediately, but that it went away simultaneous with the onset of some GI cramping and a crescendo wave of nausea. But, luckily, he did not throw up. However, he felt bad enough that he drove himself home. But partway home, he had to undo his pants' zipper to free an enormous penile erection from the constraints of his pants. He managed to get into his bedroom and lay on his back while the erection waxed and waned for the next eight hours. The most intense nausea passed early on, and by the time his wife Trudy returned home in the late afternoon, he was feeling much better but was still "a little queasy." But he still had the erection, now entirely freed from any clothing constraint and apparently enjoying the cool breezes from the air conditioning. This sight caused his wife to shriek when she came into their bedroom. Trudy said: "My God, Mac, are you all right?" And Mac replied: "I still feel a little sick, but we're going to be rich!"

By this time, I could tell all the typing and phone calls had stopped in the outer office, but Mac persisted. "You know, I'm not a young man anymore, and with my blood pressure meds, I haven't had an erection like that in a long time. In fact, I don't think I've EVER had an erection that lasted so long." I got up and closed my office door, something I should have done much earlier, but I had no idea where this conversation was going to go. Undeterred, Mac went on: "It alternated between just softly erect and a frying pan handle." Dear God, I hoped my office door was thick enough. After a moment, I gathered my thoughts and asked about any other side effects, to which he said no. I didn't tell him what was racing through my mind was the obvious violations of medical ethics, human subject's rules, and NIH guidelines, as the drug was being developed under a grant from the National Cancer Institute, and how was I going to write that into the assessment paper!

I finally thought to ask an obvious pharmacy question and that was how he determined the dose to inject himself with since this was an entirely different molecule from MT-1. Mac explained that he'd calculated the dose using a molecular weight similar to MT-1. Uh-oh. I told him something he knew but must have forgotten in the excitement of the "experiment." I said: "Mac, MT-2 has only seven amino acids. MT-1 has thirteen amino acids." What that meant was MT-2 had roughly half the molecular weight of MT-1. Doing a molar conversion for the two peptides using the molecular weight of MT-1 meant that Mac had given himself an approximate double dose of MT-2. That probably explained the more severe gastrointestinal symptoms and the prolonged erection. In later studies with MT-2, we actually validated the appropriate dose of MT-2 as being about half of what Mac had injected himself with. When Mac finally left the office, I could feel the stares and side glances from all of the female staff members in the outer office pool. One can only imagine what they were thinking. That afternoon I carefully let my own admin in on the "experiment" and explained that no, Professor Hadley is not a sex fiend.

So that started the ball rolling for the further development of MT-2, which was subsequently tested in human volunteers under strict protocols and consents. Indeed, the FDA required us to file a detailed separate Investigational New Drug Application (IND) for MT-2 since we were going down an entirely new therapeutic avenue, from skin tanning to male sexual function. The later studies in men eventually validated the erectogenic effects of the drug in normal male subjects and in men with erectile dysfunction. But we were unaware at the time that we had discovered the unknown role of a subtype of α-MSH receptors in the brains of both men and women. Thus, we didn't know at the time that MT-2 did not work directly on the penis, like Viagra. It works in the brain to cause sexual excitation of both males AND females. However, our initial findings with MT-2 led to a metabolite of MT-2, now sold commercially as bremelanotide (Vyleesi).

Vyleesi was approved by the FDA for marketing in the USA on June 21, 2019, for low sexual desire in women and is known as the "Female Viagra" and was commercially launched by AMAG Pharmaceuticals in September after being developed by Palatin Technologies. It is the first on-demand SQ injection to treat a condition of low sexual desire and mental distress in premenopausal women, a condition known as hypoactive sexual desire disorder.

Another melanotropic peptide, setmelanotide, also stimulates the same brain receptor as MT-2 and Vyleesi. Setmelanotide was approved by the FDA in November 2020 as a treatment for some rare forms of pediatric obesity (overweight children). Overall, these melanotropins represent an entirely new class of drugs with diverse properties that go far beyond tanning to include sexual function, obesity, and other newly developed experimental applications in immunology and inflammation. The age of the melanotropins is upon us.

# Chapter 3

## *Melanotan Corporation Is Born*

*This is Terry with the story of the creation of the start-up company*

In a rare display of bipartisan legislation, the US Congress passed a landmark Act in 1980 known as the Bayh-Dole Act, which allowed universities to own the results of research that was funded by the US government, which funds most university medical research. The main caveat is that the US government retains a non-exclusive license to the technology for its own use. Since they could now keep the profits from these enterprises, the Act stimulated the latent entrepreneurial spirits of university researchers and encouraged them to form companies around promising research. The universities quickly learned that they needed to share the fruits of the technology with the founders of the companies and their departments. Every university handles this differently, but most have equal sharing between the university, company founders, and the department where the research was performed. As a result, thousands of companies have now been formed by university faculty members to commercialize their research. Many useful and sometimes lifesaving products have resulted, and in the process, some enormous wealth has been created, making this Act one of the most productive pieces of legislation ever passed by Congress.

In 1981 I had the incredible fortune to accidently fall into the venture capital business. This was the time of the Reagan revolution, and I was employed by Diamond Shamrock Corporation, an oil and chemicals company that was benefiting from the second oil shock. They decided that they were going to get so much money from the increased price of oil that they needed to get into the venture capital business to invest it all. I was in the right place at the right time to be one of the two people selected to manage this effort. I learned fast, and after a couple of years, I left Diamond Shamrock and joined a group in Denver, Columbine Venture Funds, that was raising money to do our own private venture capital fund.

We were five partners, managing about eighty million dollars to invest in early stage companies, and we saw the Bayh-Dole Act as a wonderful opportunity to form some great companies, primarily in the medical field. The only problem was that a lot of other venture capitalists had the same idea, and you tripped over them on the steps of Harvard, Stanford, and MIT. So, we decided to go where others weren't, and we focused on the mid-tier universities where there is just as good science but not much competition. Over the next fifteen years, we ended up founding and/or investing in twenty-one university start-ups from fifteen different universities, mostly in the western United States.

In scouting the universities for good opportunities, we used a variety of techniques to access the key people concerned. One of the places that was high on our list was the University of Arizona in Tucson, because of its excellent medical school. However, the university had its own ideas about how to capitalize on the Bayh-Dole opportunity and hired a technology transfer officer in the late '80s and formed its own small venture capital fund. It also signed up with University Patents Inc. (UPI), which was an entity formed to work with universities to commercialize their patents and technology. UPI's business model was to pay for the patenting of university technology that they considered had potential for commercialization and then to share in any income which came from the licensing of these patents. This included both cash license fees and ownership in any company formed to commercialize the technology. This made it more difficult for us to access the opportunities at U of A, and it took a while for us to be taken seriously.

We continued to work with the university's technology transfer officer and looked at several opportunities, none of which we felt had commercial potential. However, in June 1991 I was introduced to the co-author of this book, Bob Dorr, and he described the Melanotan technology. I was immediately hooked! The problem was that the technology was encumbered by a lawsuit that was in progress over the ownership of the technology. However, it sounded so promising that we agreed to work together to try to create a possible deal that we could implement when the lawsuit was settled and the technology available. Unfortunately, this lawsuit seriously dampened the university's enthusiasm for participating in these commercial ventures and had an influence on the structure of the company that we eventually set up, causing the university to refuse any ownership in the company.

We had numerous meetings with Bob and the Melanotan researchers over the next eighteen months and also worked with UPI to explore the scope of a possible deal. It soon became obvious that there were many issues to address and decisions to be made. We had a candy store of possible drug candidates and a variety of very interesting targets including tanning, sexual stimulation, and weight loss, with all three of these indications being present in some of the molecules. Any of these indications would be capable of building a multibillion-dollar company, and there were no competitive products that were effective in any of these three fields (Viagra had not been launched yet). We also had to determine who would be the founders of the company, the roles they would play, how to reward the university and UPI for making the technology available to the new company, find a founding CEO to run the company, determine the clinical and business strategies, and then figure out how to raise the money and start to build a management team. This was a daunting list and took some time to sort out.

Before we could proceed to create and fund a company, there was a lot of diligence that had to be done to be sure that there were no obvious issues that would stand in the way of developing a successful company. We looked at the market issues, did reference checks on the people, made sure that the patents and intellectual property were valid and free of infringement, and reviewed all the science that had been done to date, especially some of the animal work that could foretell side effects of the potential drugs in humans that may cause them to fail.

We were slowly getting more comfortable with the technology, the people, and the market opportunity, and we reviewed all aspects at an all-hands meeting in Tucson on December 18, 1992. There were over a dozen university people who spent some time with me at this all-day meeting, and we reviewed all the scientific and clinical work which had been done on the project to that time. It was at this meeting that I developed a deep respect for everybody involved, and I realized that we were dealing with outstanding science and scientists. With the university's limited resources, they had done everything necessary to take the drug through the equivalent of a phase one clinical trial but using what is known as an Investigator-Sponsored (Physician's) - Investigational New Drug (P-IND) filing with the FDA. This is not as stringent as a normal IND as filed by drug companies, but it ends up giving you the same kinds of results, primarily an assessment of safety in human patients and an indication of efficacy. The results were positive on both counts, and the work had actually been published in the prestigious Journal of the American Medical Association in 1991. This not only involved dealing with the FDA but also arranging to have relatively large amounts of the drug made for the study and finding and treating patients, activities that were not usually done at universities.

It was also obvious that the driving force for the science was provided by Dr. Victor Hruby, an eminent peptide chemist who had a gold-plated background working with many of the leaders in the field. We were indeed fortunate to have stumbled across this opportunity, and it was evident that in this field, the University of Arizona is a world leader.

Normally, at this point in putting together a company, there can be very long delays in working out the structure of who gets how much ownership and the details of the licensing deal for the technology. But this part of the project proceeded smoothly since everyone was very reasonable and businesslike, and the licensing deal had already been worked out by the university directly with UPI. We were able to agree on a deal by about the middle of 1993. Because they were traumatized by the lawsuit in progress, the university did not want any ownership and simply suggested that we assign 40 percent of their ownership to UPI and distribute the balance between the founding scientists. We worked out some numbers and proceeded to work with these on founding the company. In summary, we agreed to make an initial seed investment of two hundred thousand dollars for 13 percent of the company, with UPI at 18 percent and the three founders with 9 percent each, leaving 42 percent of the company unassigned and earmarked for future management. All of this, of course, was subject to dilution from raising additional money which, depending on the price that it was raised at, would dilute everyone's position. These numbers are quite normal in these kinds of investments. Since UPI had funded all the patents, they got most of the future royalties and were happy with maximizing their ownership with no cash up front. It is always important to minimize cash outflow in these seed investments, and my partners felt that these terms were fair to everyone.

It seems that there was no disagreement at the university about who should be the founders. In addition to a reward for their work in developing the technology, these founders agreed to help the company to move forward in their field of expertise:

Dr. Robert Dorr has already been profiled and is co-author of this book. He was the driving force among the three founders to create the company. He was a pharmacologist at the university and specialized in the development of cancer chemotherapy products.

Dr. Mac Hadley has also already been profiled in chapter two. He was Professor of Anatomy at the university and did much of the animal work on the effect of the drug candidates.

Dr. Norman Levine was the third founder. He was a practicing clinical dermatologist at the university and was responsible for leading the initial human clinical trials of the Melanotan-1 drug candidate.

So now we were almost ready to create the company, but the last step was to hire several expert consultants to give us a final review, including my good friend Dr. Randy Steer, an MD/PhD physician/scientist whom we had worked with many times in the past. After he had completed his review, Randy called me:

"Terry, I really like the people, the drugs, and the market, but there is one crucial question that needs to be addressed before I can give you a green light to proceed, and that is whether these drug candidates somehow cause or promote the growth of cancers, particularly melanoma. They have such a wide variety of activities that this is going to be one of the first questions that FDA asks before they allow you to go into clinical trials. I know you like the tanning opportunity best, and I think that is where you should focus to answer this question."

"But, Randy, this requires us to prove a negative, that the drug does not cause cancer, and you know how difficult it is to prove a negative. You are always just one experiment away from an adverse result, so how many studies do we have to do to prove this to FDA's satisfaction?"

"That's a difficult question to answer, but I suggest that you get with the university people and come up with all the experiments you can think of to test whether melanocytes are turned into melanoma or other skin cancer cells by the drug or if it causes the melanoma cancer cells to grow faster. Then we can review the results and see if we can put together a good case. I don't think this is a slam-dunk, and we are going to have to put together a good package."

"Okay, Randy, we will get on it and be back to you when the work is done."

I immediately called Bob Dorr. He was already ahead of us on this issue and had a program worked out, but it needed significant funding. After a lot of discussion, we felt that it was best to proceed to form the company and to make the performance of this work one of the things in the budget that this seed investment would support. Some of the work was to be done at the university, but the majority of it was to be done by independent outside laboratories, because we needed results from neutral third parties that were unbiased.

We contacted our lawyers and proceeded to form the company, which was completed in December 1993. Columbine Venture Funds, our investor where I was a general partner, was comfortable with taking on the risk of the work to be performed on the cancer effects and also with the risk of the outstanding lawsuit that affected part of the technology. Progress had been made by the university to resolve the lawsuit, and we felt that this was no longer a significant risk. The tanning application was clear of the lawsuit, and it only involved some of the other indications for the technology.

The management of the company in the early stages through proof of principle was quite easy to resolve since we were pioneering a strategy of building several virtual pharmaceutical companies under one roof in an early stage incubator where the team would handle the development of several products. We were working with Dr. Hank Agersborg to build a small staff to handle the early proof of principle work for several of these virtual companies in an incubator near Philadelphia, Pennsylvania, and we already had two companies in the incubator with room for a third. Hank was an impressive individual who had recently retired after an outstanding career in drug development primarily with American Home Products' Wyeth Ayerst where he had run their pharmaceutical R&D. He had a dour personality and resembled WC Fields in both looks and mannerisms. But he was truly an expert in dealing with the FDA and all the other aspects of drug development. Thus, he acted as CEO of all three incubator companies.

So, by the end of 1993, we had these key issues sorted out and had the legal documents all in order. The final step was to create a board of directors. This can be sensitive in these start-up companies since there are usually more candidates than spaces available. Everyone, especially university executives, wants the prestige of being a board member. However, in this case, the board came together naturally since the university did not want to be represented; we only had one investor, Columbine; we had a seasoned CEO; and a technology provider, UPI, with much small company experience, and so, the board consisted of Hank Agersborg, CEO; Sid Alpert, UPI; and Terry Winters, Columbine. This also fulfilled the need for a board where the members were willing to roll up their sleeves to make the company work, and I'm happy to report that the board functioned well right from the beginning in providing oversight and guidance on strategy so necessary in these fledgling small companies. The new company was officially formed in December 1993, and Melanotan Corporation began its life with its first board meeting on December 22, 1993.

# Chapter 4

## *Preparing to Raise Funds*

*Terry continues with the things that had to be done before we could raise funding.*

Now that we were over the hurdles of creating the company, we had to figure out exactly what we had and whether we could mold it into a coherent story to raise the considerable amount of money needed to run all the clinical trials to satisfy the FDA requirements for approving and, ultimately, marketing a new drug. We used the first six months of 1994 to define the seed stage milestones and to learn all we could about the melanocortin molecules and the possible clinical indications where we could make a difference and get approval to market the drug. We had a lot of work to do before the company was ready to begin fundraising.

The objective of the first board meeting of Melanotan Inc. in December 1993 was to work out the final details of the company formation and structure. Then, at the next meeting in January 1994, we prioritized the things that must get done before we could write the business plan and start serious fundraising. Although we only had three board members, the founders sat in on all the meetings and were an integral part of the board discussion.

You may wonder why it was necessary to get new investors for the fundraising, and the answer is that this is the normal way of operating in the early seed stage venture capital investment business. We were quite comfortable with making a small seed investment of up to about $250,000 and taking on the formation of the company with several well-defined risks. But to invest more than that amount needs validation of at least one additional venture capital investor. It's a very good way to confirm that we are not making a bad mistake and that someone else also believes that it is a good investment. The rule was that our fund could commit to invest in the second round but could not implement it without a substantial new investor to validate it. In this case, we invested two hundred thousand dollars initially and kept back fifty thousand to invest if more time and work were needed. Then we committed one million dollars to the next investment round that could only be implemented when a new investor joined us with at least the same amount.

The things which needed to be done were defined and prioritized. This was a daunting list of seed stage milestones, especially with only two hundred thousand dollars' funding to do all these tasks. However, this is why most innovations come from small companies in the pharmaceutical business because the big companies would have taken several years and spent tens of millions on these items. We had limited people and funds and set ourselves only a year to get answers and then to make a decision to move forward or not. We could do this because of the commitment of all concerned and the incredible hard work, commitment, and resourcefulness of our University of Arizona (UA) partners, the founders, and the small staff at Hank's incubator in Philadelphia. They were terrific, very focused and tireless in their quest to help people with a potentially amazing new drug. What is commitment? It is best illustrated by a plate of ham and eggs—the chicken was involved, but the pig was committed!

So, here is the prioritized list with a summary of the progress in the first year, to end 1995:

1. **Confirm Melanotan-1 does not cause or promote skin cancer.**

   This was our first priority: Complete the work, mostly done by independent laboratories, to show that Melanotan-1 does not cause skin cells to become malignant or accelerate the growth or proliferation of already cancerous cells. If this was not successful, we would not have a company.

   The UA founders were plugged into all the leaders in the dermatology community, and we decided to contract out the work to five different laboratories, all of them carefully selected to be independent of the company. We reasoned that doing it this way would insulate us from accusations of bias and make the resulting work more credible. Randy Steer reviewed the whole program and commented that this was more supporting work than goes into a typical New Drug Application (NDA).

This program was the largest single item of expenditure from our seed funding since it was the crucial question that could kill the drug. At our fund, we used to joke that our real business was trying to kill drugs since we always set out to find out first if there were any serious issues that would prevent the drug from gaining FDA approval or would make it uncompetitive in the market, in which case we could walk away with only a small loss and not waste money on further development of a drug that was not going to be successful. This would also save us time that could be devoted to more productive efforts.

After this work program was initiated, we held our breath as the results came in, which took about three months. Luckily, none of the tests yielded a positive result, and we could safely conclude that these drugs did not cause or promote the growth of cancer and, specifically, skin cancer. Randy Steer signed off on this issue in July 1994, saying that we had now amassed enough data to stand a very good chance of convincing the FDA that this is not an issue of concern. We all breathed a collective sigh of relief and, invigorated, continued with our work.

2. **Settle the lawsuit and define our intellectual property (IP).**

We needed to have the lawsuit against the university resolved to determine the intellectual property rights that we could be granted. Ideally, we would like the rights to tanning, sexual arousal, and satiety indications.

In a stroke of good fortune, our wishes were granted when we got the news in late February 1994 that the main lawsuit between the university and the plaintiffs was settled. Basically, the university had unknowingly sold the same thing to two different parties and had to make amends. For a payment of six million dollars, they got all the rights to the technology back and were free to license them to us since it seemed that everybody else had lost interest. We then had our choice of which of the three main technologies, tanning, sexual arousal, and satiety (weight loss), to license into the company. We chose to take all three but to focus first on tanning. A license agreement was quickly negotiated, and the second of the major risk factors in our seed investment was settled.

There was no upfront cash payment, only the granting of stock to UPI, a modest annual cash payment to keep the license active, and a reasonable royalty on sales after the product was approved and launched. We were amazed that no one else was interested in the technology and couldn't believe our good fortune.

We needed to focus and could not handle multiple drug development programs at the same time since we did not have the people nor the capital to pursue such a strategy. But we also needed to raise money and were willing to change our strategy to accommodate the interests of our potential investors, and so, taking all three technologies made sense with an initial focus on tanning and the ability to change focus to the other areas if the new investors demanded it.

3. **Select molecules to develop and explore dose, safety, and efficacy.**

We decided to continue the small clinical trials at the university and initiate pre-clinical animal studies to get a better idea of the dose, safety, and efficacy of the drugs.

The patent estate that we had now licensed included literally thousands of molecules that were variations on the structure of natural α-MSH. These variations were created by substituting the thirteen amino acids in the chain of α-MSH with the other twenty natural amino acids and their optical isomers. But there were really only two serious drug candidates which had been identified from measurement of the properties of the candidates. We called these Melanotan-1 and -2.

Melanotan-1 is, like α-MSH, a thirteen-amino acid straight-chain (linear) peptide with two new amino acid substitutions. It had been shown in the frog skin pigmentation assay to be much more potent in tanning than α-MSH and to be about one hundred times more stable in the blood. This is a very important property to be a commercial drug. As a linear peptide, it had the two ends free, which made it strongly polar, positive at one end and negative at the other end, and so prevented it from crossing the blood/brain barrier and causing the brain-mediated side effects seen with some of the other molecules. As a result, it was not active in sexual arousal nor satiety but was specific for tanning, potentially making it a very good and safe drug.

Melanotan-2 was different since it was structured as a ring, a cyclic seven-amino acid peptide where the two ends had reacted together to form a circular molecule. It was therefore smaller in size, effectively non-polar, and it could easily cross the blood/brain barrier. This enabled it to act on many centers in the brain thereby giving rise to multiple potential side effects. Due to these multiple effects, Hank, especially, had his doubts whether this could ever be a viable drug, but we agreed to proceed with testing to see what we could do with it.

We initiated preclinical testing of both molecules, MT-1 and MT-2, in animals, which would be required for the FDA to allow us to start human trials that would count in the long approval process. The team at Hank's incubator handled this work, and the standout result was that when Melanotan-2 was injected into female rabbits, they adopted the copulation position. This really impressed us, and we speculated that if we could overcome side effects, this would be a dramatic drug. However, these were the days before Viagra, and many of us were concerned about the social acceptability of such a drug and wondered if we could ever get something like this to be accepted in the marketplace. This seems to be somewhat quaint in hindsight, but it was a major concern at the time and reminds us that Viagra was a huge step forward in social acceptance.

The small trials in humans under the physician's IND were handled by the founding team and other faculty members at the university, and they developed information that was very useful to us as we went forward. None of this could be used in the formal trial process to get approval for the drugs, but it could be used as part of the package to write the Investigational New Drug (IND) Application, which would be necessary to initiate the formal clinical trials in humans.

4. **Define quality of the tan.**

Confirm that the tan induced by the drugs is fully equivalent to a natural tan.

This was easy to do and involved injecting the drug into a human volunteer, spectroscopically measuring the darkening of the skin and then comparing this to naturally tanned people. The artificially tanned people were then followed for six months to determine how their tans faded away and compared to controls whose skins had been tanned by exposure to the sun. It was obvious that there was no difference between the groups and that the tan induced by the drug was fully equivalent to a natural tan both in formation and as it slowly faded away.

5. **Initiate the work on a controlled release version of the tanning drug.**

   This work was done by one of the faculty members at the university who had substantial pharmaceutical experience in slow-release injectable formulations. The work gave us the basic information to enable us to later contract out development of a controlled release version to one of the companies who specialized in this.

6. **Define strategy and focus.**

   Create a strategy for the company including the initial focus area and selection of the first clinical indication.

   This was the source of much debate at the board and management levels, which is covered later in this chapter.

7. **Write a business plan and begin fundraising.**

   By the summer of 1994, we felt that most of the key risks had been addressed, and it was now time to write a business plan, which is the fundamental document of private fundraising.

We learned a great deal during this process, and at times, my head was spinning with all the new information. Here are a few things we learned:

- The pigmented substance that causes tanning, melanin, exists in reddish and black pigments known as pheomelanin and eumelanin, respectively. The melanocytes in human skin, depending on your genetic inheritance, are capable of producing both and the blend of the two causes the wide variety of different coloring in nature. The natural melanocyte stimulating hormone (α-MSH) stimulates the melanocytes to make melanin. The ratio of pheomelanin and eumelanin is determined by genetics, with pheomelanin being much less photoprotective against sun damage.

- Humans are unusual in that we have melanocytes in our skin and in our hair follicles. Most animals only have them in their hair follicles, which we saw clearly when Melanotan-2 drug was injected into a white dog and a band of black coloring slowly grew out into its hair. One exception in the animal world is the frog, and the melanocytes (actually melanophores) in their skin can be used as an indicator for the tanning effect of the drug candidates. The photos on page 91-97 capture these effects in frogs and the dog.
- The university had proceeded very carefully with their phase-one trial in student volunteers to watch for side effects, but apart from some initial facial flushing, nothing significant had been seen. There was an obvious increase in skin darkening of the students with increasing dose and an increased (synergistic) effect with sun exposure had been noted.
- The half-life in blood of natural α-MSH is about one minute, and the Melanotan-1 drug candidate is about thirty minutes. While this much longer life of Melanotan-1 makes it a viable drug, after injection, very little was left in the blood after two hours. As a result, the university scientists were recommending that we develop a slow release dose that would have a longer lasting effect. We realized that this would be time consuming and expensive and decided to start this work as soon as we had raised sufficient funds, but meanwhile, we continued with the single daily dose trials.
- They had also tried delivering the drug by mouth and transdermally (across the skin), but without success. It was quickly destroyed in the stomach and did not pass through the skin. Therefore, the slow release injectable dose seemed to be the best way to proceed.
- The patent situation was complicated, as is usually the case, but it looked like we had good patent protection as composition of matter and use patents through to about 2005. As you will see in a later chapter, a very fortunate observation related to the controlled release formulation extended this patent life well into the 2020s.

The most difficult part of creating the business strategy for the company was selecting the medical application in humans that we would need to use in the clinical trial to gain approval to market the product. Approval to market is only granted by the FDA for a specific clinical application, and you cannot get approval simply for changing some kind of condition in the human body such as tanning, unless this condition has clearly been shown to correlate with some improved health outcome for the patient. The classic example is blood pressure reduction where the decrease in blood pressure has been unequivocally shown to cause less heart attacks and strokes, and so, any new blood pressure drug only has to show that it can decrease blood pressure to gain approval. Its effect on the clinical condition of heart attacks and strokes is then assumed to be positive.

Our deliberations were complicated by the history of another drug, Botox, which has become a blockbuster drug through being prescribed for use in cosmetic indications such as facial wrinkles although it was never approved for this and was originally only approved as a therapy for an obscure, rare orphan condition. This was possible since the FDA can't control prescribing of a drug once it is approved for any indication. After the initial approval, any drug can be prescribed for any condition by any physician. However, the drug cannot be promoted for such off-label conditions, a limitation that is currently under attack at the FDA, as it may be construed to be a violation of the free-speech amendment to the US Constitution. It was generally thought that FDA regrets this situation and would never allow it to happen again, i.e., allowing a drug to be prescribed for cosmetic use after only being approved for a small orphan indication.

We had long debates about the strategy to bring the drug to market for the most benefit to most patients. We all agreed that we did not want to be the guinea pigs to test the off-label use situation at FDA; therefore, if we targeted the cosmetic market, we would have to do specific trials which would probably take several thousand patients and have very stringent safety requirements. This would certainly maximize the market size, but it would also maximize the amount of money we would need to get the drug to market and increase the risks.

This decision was made even more difficult by the accidental publicity we started to get and the people who contacted the company. When we formalized this with a website and included a form that could be filled out and sent in to request participation in our clinical trials, we got an avalanche of interest from the public, specifically in the tanning application for cosmetic uses. In fact, of all the investments I have ever made, this one got the most consumer interest. It seems that people are fascinated with the possibility of changing their skin color, which was probably not so surprising when you consider that over six thousand tanning salons are already in business in the USA.

However, at the time, biotechnology was very much out of favor in North America. These were the years of the Clinton presidency, and the economy was not doing well after his huge tax increase. Coupled with the poor track record of many biotechnology companies that had gone public in the early 1990s, it was very difficult to raise money for drug development companies. Remember that this was before the time of increased drug prices and of the availability of abundant capital. The huge rise in drug prices, the great recession of 2008/9, central bank largesse and quantitative easing, leading to abundant capital, were all in the not-too-distant future, but not visible to us at that time. After long debates by the Melanotan board of directors, we agreed that going directly for the cosmetic indication was not viable and that we should focus on the tanning drug but also take the sexual arousal and satiety drugs as a back-up to see if we could get interest from investors in one of the three areas, in which case we may have to change our focus. We decided that in light of the very poor financial market conditions, we should minimize the amount of capital we were attempting to raise by focusing on a clinical condition, which would require a relatively low-cost trial in a specialty orphan indication. But such an indication was not obvious.

As we proceeded along the drug development path, this was going to be a continuing, and sometimes heated, debate as to whether we should focus on the cosmetic or the clinical indications. But in this first instance, the decision was made for us by the very tight availability of capital.

Having made the decision to focus on an orphan clinical indication, we now had to select the appropriate indication, and we spent a considerable amount of time looking at the options. But before we finalized the indication, we still had to figure out whether we could induce enough of a tanning effect to make the drug a commercial proposition. This turned out to be much more difficult than we expected and will be addressed in more detail later.

We need to take a detour for a moment and explain what we mean by an "orphan" drug. Remember that these were the days before the explosive rise in drug prices, and therefore, all the drug companies were focused on developing drugs for very large markets in terms of patient numbers. This was the only way that they could generate the revenues necessary to pay for the very high cost of drug development since they just could not afford to squander their resources on drugs for indications with very small numbers of patients where they could never get a return on their investment. So, enter the US Congress with the bipartisan Orphan Drug Act of 1983, which has turned out to be one of the most successful Acts they have ever passed. It instructed the FDA to create an orphan drug category for new drugs in development that address markets of less than two hundred thousand patients per year.

Drugs in the orphan category are granted an automatic seven years of marketing exclusivity on approval, special development grants, and tax incentives. More importantly, the FDA was instructed by Congress to interpret the regulations for orphan drug approval with maximum flexibility. While the approval standards were not changed for orphan drugs, the practical result was that they could be approved with just a single clinical trial protocol and usually with small numbers of patients compared to the two protocols and larger patient numbers required for other drugs. The seven years of exclusivity was also a major incentive because it is equivalent to a patent and prevents any competition for that period. In several ways, it is better than a patent since many drugs come to market with only seven years or less of their patent time remaining, and orphan drug exclusivity is not subject to the vagaries of patent law.

As intended, this Act had the effect of making it profitable for companies to develop drugs for these orphan indications, and now, at the end of 2019, over three hundred orphan drugs have been approved and over five hundred more are currently in clinical trials. Thousands of lives have been saved and many patients have been spared from a life of suffering as a result of this legislation. However, no one foresaw what has become an even greater incentive to develop orphan drugs, and that is the very high prices they now command. These high prices developed slowly as the pharmaceutical industry carefully probed the sensitivity of the private insurers to higher and higher prices. The first such orphan drug crossed the threshold of one hundred thousand dollars per patient per year in the late '90s, and now, per-patient prices of over three hundred thousand dollars per year are commonplace. This has had the effect of turning really small markets of just a few thousand patients per year into large revenue markets that can justify a lot of development dollars, with even more patient benefits. Europe, therefore, followed with its own orphan drug act in 2000, and the rest of the world is also getting on board.

In looking at clinical conditions that could be addressed by a tanning drug, I was amazed at the wide variety of skin diseases. Some of those we considered were:

- Albinism. No pigment is produced resulting in people with very white skin and hair. This is a rare condition that would easily qualify as an orphan drug
- Vitiligo. Irregular areas without pigment, frequently on the face and arms, that can be disfiguring. This is now known as Michael Jackson disease and is caused by dysfunctional or absent melanocytes in the affected areas. This constitutes a relatively common condition and a high patient need, but not a candidate for orphan designation.
- Sun allergy, also known as polymorphous light eruption, or PMLE.
- Porphyria, especially erythropoetic protoporphyria or EPP. The porphyrias are orphan diseases caused by genetic defects in making hemoglobin. The EPP type of porphyria causes agonizing pain in patients when they venture out into the sun, and it is rare enough to be an orphan disease.
- Skin cancer prevention. We perceived this as a very difficult target where the clinical trials would take many years and be very expensive. However, the huge difference in the incidence of skin cancers in white and black populations showed that it would probably work. At the time we didn't know that prevention of skin cancer in transplant patients would become so important since organ transplants were just beginning to become established clinical practice.

There was no standout indication for Melanotan-1 in tanning where we could see a clear need, a high chance of success, and an obvious development pathway, and so, we spent a lot of time digging into these and other indications. We had a unique way of creating tanned skin, but we were still a solution looking for a problem. When we turned to Melanotan-2 in sexual arousal and appetite suppression applications, we could see much clearer indications, but we were still very concerned about the side effects of a drug that crossed the blood/brain barrier, and Hank continued to warn of these dangers to getting approval. With his massive experience in the drug business, his caution made us very nervous.

But money and time were running out, and we had to make a decision on the way to go. So, without true conviction, we settled on PMLE and albinism as our candidates and proceeded to write the plan with these as the main targets and with skin cancer prevention, erectile dysfunction, and satiety thrown in for good measure, if the investors liked these better. As things transpired, this was much too wide a menu of targets and made potential investors nervous. But now, with the business plan written, it was time to try to raise funds and see if the world was interested enough for someone to risk investment capital for us to move forward.

# Chapter 5
## *Fundraising*

*Terry reports on coming up dry on fundraising.*

This will be a very short chapter since our efforts to raise funds in 1995 and 1996 were a dismal failure. Part of the reason for this failure can be ascribed to the market and the political situation in the US. These were the early Bill Clinton days with the fallout from his large tax increase making investors very nervous about committing funds for what they regarded as high-risk ventures. Of note, Clinton later pivoted and reduced taxes, which greatly spurred the economy, but that was not what we faced at the time of our fundraising needs.

There had been a lot of biotechnology public offerings in the early 1990s. But the bottom had then fallen out of that market, and this was a strong headwind to raising money for yet another biotechnology company. That was especially true for this one, which proposed creating peptide drugs, which was quite novel at the time. I remember one of my biotechnology venture capitalist acquaintances showing me his portfolio of public biotechnology companies where the stock of every one of them was not only priced below their Initial Public Offering (IPO) share price but below his fund's entry level, pre-IPO share price, as well! He said that in this climate, it was impossible to convince his partners to do another biotechnology deal.

However, in hindsight, the main problem was that we had a solution searching for a problem. And we did not have a clear vision of the specific clinical indication that we would pursue to get the product approved and on the market. Further, we had not optimized the drug delivery method to get a strong tanning result; we were still persevering with the single daily injection of MT-1 as a liquid solution. And we had not progressed with developing the slow release implant to the point where we could get any human clinical trial results. To us, the fact that we could induce a tan in humans that was equivalent to a natural tan was a major breakthrough, and it was obvious that there would be many uses for such a product. But investors thought otherwise and voted with their feet. They did not like the weight-loss indication and were also nervous of the sexual arousal indication, pointing out that it would have a negative social reaction; Viagra had not yet come along to test those waters. This all seems rather strange with the benefit of hindsight, but when you are living through these future development unknowns, it is very real and explains why innovation can be so very difficult.

This was also the time when the internet bubble was just beginning to take off, and this sucked much of the air out of investing in biotechnology and new drugs in favor of internet things, such as the dot.com companies.

So, the first phase of developing the tanning drug came to a quiet end in 1996, but it was not a sudden ending where we took the company into bankruptcy. Fortunately, we did not have any debts nor creditors, and so, the company just passed into a state of inactivity, and we all moved on to doing other things, leaving it sitting there and ready for the next exciting phase, even though we did not realize that there would be life after this unfortunate beginning.

# Chapter 6
## *Australia Beckons*

*Terry tells how Australia entered the story.*

After I finished my PhD in chemistry at the University of Wales in Swansea, UK, in 1967, I immediately took off to do a postdoctoral fellowship at University of California Los Angeles (UCLA). This was the accepted thing to do for an academic science career, and I took the recommendation of my thesis adviser professor to go to UCLA. I had kept my nose to the grindstone for three years to complete the PhD and, frankly, hadn't paid much attention to what happened next. My PhD subject was the synthesis of the tetracycline antibiotics; the work that I did for a year at UCLA was isolating possible drug candidates from California desert plants, both in the field of natural product research. We went on field trips to the desert east of Los Angeles to gather samples and then came back to the lab, ground them up, and tried to extract any chemicals of interest. UCLA at the time had a powerhouse chemistry department that had four Nobel prize winners on its faculty. It was a great place to be.

This was my first time in the United States, and everything was new to me. Frankly, I was confused and bewildered, especially with the sports, which were like nothing we had in England where soccer and rugby were the main sports. In those days at UCLA, there were big playing fields next to the football and basketball stadiums. Soon after I arrived, I met another guy, an Australian doing a postdoctoral fellowship in biochemistry, while kicking a ball around on the playing fields. We struck up an instant friendship and both expressed an interest in seeing if we could learn to play American football. We went into the UCLA stadium and asked a guy who looked like he was on the staff if we could apply to play for one of the UCLA football teams. We simply assumed that it was like the UK and Australia where the universities had four or five teams that played competitively against the similar tiered team at other universities. He gave us an icy stare and said that there is only one team, and it was most unlikely that we would qualify. We left with our hopes crushed, but it cemented our friendship.

My new friend was Wayne Millen, who hailed from Perth, Australia, and had just completed his PhD. We had apartments close together and spent a lot of time together, with our wives, during this year of research. And we stayed in contact after we left UCLA. Wayne had a wonderful sense of humor that meshed very well with my London humor. He was a very good tennis player and a much better athlete than me, but we had a lot in common, especially with our outlook on our future careers. During this postdoctoral year, we both decided that the academic life was not for us and that we were far more interested in business.

That outlook was not very popular with our professors, but after we left UCLA in 1968, I joined Goodyear in Akron, Ohio. I became a polymer chemist and then went into their international business, buying and selling technology worldwide. After the first oil shock in 1978, I joined Diamond Shamrock in Cleveland, Ohio. I was put in their technology licensing department, finding new technology to buy as the basis for new businesses. Eventually, in 1983, I became a venture capitalist with Columbine Venture Funds, a private partnership in Denver, investing in biotechnology companies, a new area just getting started.

After UCLA, Wayne went back to his native Perth in Australia and founded a mining analysis company. He sold it after about ten years, thereby making a lot of money. We stayed in contact, which was not easy in those pre-internet days, and I visited him in Perth several times. I thought Perth was a paradise on earth, but that is another story. Wayne was curious about my activities, and he got very interested in venture capital investing, and so, as I mentioned earlier, we invited him to the annual meeting of our venture fund, Columbine Ventures, in 1996 in Vail, Colorado. At that meeting, Hank was presenting the three companies that were in our pharmaceutical company incubator, which included Melanotan Inc. and other companies developing an anti-inflammatory drug and a nerve desensitization drug.

After the presentation, Wayne literally ran across the room, grabbed me by my neck, and, shaking me so that I would not forget it, said that he wanted to be involved with Melanotan because this is exactly what Australian investors are looking for. The skin cancer problem in Australia is so serious that anything that can alleviate it would command a major market. Ideally, he would like to take the company to Australia, set it up there, and get it financed. I got the message and said that I would see what we could do.

Three years later, in 1999, we had not been able to raise funds to move Melanotan forward in the US, and it was dormant. Wayne called to check in and remind me of his interest, and when he learned that we had stopped work on it, he badgered me to somehow get him involved. I was reluctant to initiate something half a world away since it seemed like a lot of work and my plate was full of other start-up companies. But he kept calling, and I finally called Bob Dorr in Tucson. He felt that we had nothing to lose by signing it over to Wayne, under the right terms. The other Melanotan board members agreed, and we did a deal in a few months where Wayne would set up a new company in Australia, called Epitan, and we would sell him the Melanotan intellectual property rights, for tanning only, for an equity stake in Epitan that would be held in the existing Melanotan Corporate shell. The university and UPI were happy with the deal since they got back the sexual arousal and weight-loss IP that could now be licensed on to new entities, and at the beginning of 1999, the deal was done. Hank and I stayed in contact with Wayne, and I kept the three founders advised of progress. Melanotan continued as a private shell, and we maintained the board, but no further work was done on this in Tucson.

None of the Melanotan board or founders expected Wayne to be successful, and so, we didn't pay much attention to the structuring of this deal. It was sort of done in our spare time, and we regarded it as a "Hail Mary" that had a very slim chance of succeeding. None of us went to Australia to meet some of the other people or to gauge investor interest in a deal like this. We certainly did not think of consulting tax experts and simply told the lawyers what to do. I have seen many deals like this done with unsuccessful companies, and they invariably fail. So I guess that explains the lack of attention to these details. If we had been paying attention, we would have realized that, in the event of success, we were creating one huge tax problem for the Melanotan shareholders. This is because all of our Epitan shares were still within the Melanotan corporate structure. If the Epitan shares went up in value, we would eventually have to distribute them as a dividend to the Melanotan shareholders and pay tax on the appreciation in price at ordinary tax rates. And then when we eventually sold the Epitan shares, we would have to pay tax again. A great example of double taxation that we could have avoided by simply distributing the Epitan shares to the Melanotan shareholders when the deal was done and before the shares had appreciated. A small amount of tax would have been paid but very much less than we eventually had to pay.

Wayne stayed in touch with me every few months as he worked the Australian investor scene, but I regarded it as a sideshow and did not pay much attention. This was a very interesting time since we were approaching the turn of the millennium, Australia was getting ready to host the Olympic Games in 2000, and the bubble in Internet stocks was becoming more obvious. I was now a partner in both the Denver-based Columbine and Scottsdale-based Valley Ventures funds, and we were inundated with business plans about how to make a killing using the Internet. We developed a simple question which helped to keep us out of these deals, and it was simply to ask: "What are you going to make and sell, and how do you make a profit?" Since no one was paying attention to this, then no one could answer that question to our satisfaction, and we, luckily, stayed out of these deals.

In July 2000 I got the call from Wayne that has already been described in chapter one. He had raised six million (six million Australian dollars, at the time, about US three million) in a private deal. But it needed commitments from Hank and me to join the EpiTan Ltd. board of directors to proceed to closing. After Wayne did the appropriate arm twisting of both of us, the deal closed quickly, and we had our first board meeting by phone in August 2000. The plan was to complete a small initial public offering (IPO) as soon as possible so that we had a listed public stock on the Australian Stock Exchange (ASX). That would satisfy the condition that the original mezzanine investors had attached to raising their money. However, the problem was that the markets were beginning to wobble as investors slowly realized that the Internet king had no clothes on. The Epitan IPO seemed to go on forever, but it finally got done on February 13, 2001, although it raised only an additional A$1.5 million. That gave us, after expenses, about A$7 million to achieve some milestones so we could raise a lot more money later to continue the long and expensive process of developing the drug and getting approval from the US FDA, EU EMA, and other country regulatory bodies to market it for still-to-be-identified medical conditions.

The Melanotan board, management, and investors were not directly involved with this process of raising money in Australia. However, we very quickly got involved after the money had been raised so that we could understand what and how much we owned. It was a complex process in what we would call in the US a penny stock market—this was how the ASX companies conducted business. The net result of this long, drawn-out process was that the Melanotan shareholders now owned 15.1 million shares and 9.2 million options of Epitan exercisable at A$0.30/share.

An option is the right to buy a share at a fixed, defined price for a period of time, usually five years. If the company is successful and the stock price rises, then the option will be exercised with a profit to the investor and more funds for the company since the company receives the exercise price proceeds. If the stock falls, then the option expires worthless. Therefore, we potentially owned a total of 24.3 million shares less the cost of exercising the options.

The IPO funding had been raised at about A$0.1875 (about nineteen cents)/share and there were 86.4 million shares and 60.3 million options in total outstanding for a total share count, assuming all options were exercised, of about 147 million shares. Astute readers will have worked out that the fully diluted market cap at the IPO, with all options exercised, was about A$28 million, or US$14 million.

The Melanotan shareholders (Founders, UPI, Columbine, and Hank) therefore owned 17.52 percent of the shares and, if all options were exercised, 16.61% of the fully diluted shares. This result was achieved by a lot of horse trading, including the transfer of special amounts of shares from the Epitan founders to the mezzanine and public investors. Even though we were not used to this kind of a financing environment, we were satisfied that it was all done with full disclosure and high integrity, and we were happy with the outcome.

Unfortunately, the market continued to deteriorate after the IPO, and the price of the stock on the ASX bottomed at about six Australian cents per share (A$0.06), making the market cap about the same as the company's cash. Understandably, that resulted in a lot of unhappy shareholders who did not hesitate to express their dissatisfaction. I didn't realize it, but Hank and I were about to experience the full force of this unhappiness at the first annual meeting of Epitan, which was an interesting experience and is described later. But we now had the funds to continue the development program and to try to correct the share price situation.

We had had two phone meetings of the new Epitan board in August and September 2000, prior to the IPO during which the only real topic of discussion was getting the IPO done. There were five of us on the board, including Wayne, Hank, and me, with two representatives of the mezzanine investors, one of these was the chairman of the board. I didn't pick up any negative vibes in these phone meetings, and after the IPO was completed, we arranged to have an in-person meeting in Melbourne, Australia, on April 3, 2001.

We started with a board dinner the night before at a very nice restaurant on Collins Street in the middle of Melbourne's business district. Hank and I were not prepared for what happened at the dinner since we walked right into the middle of a very poisoned atmosphere with the other two board members being extremely critical of Wayne's performance as CEO. This was amazing to us and most inappropriate at a get-to-know-you dinner. We were surprised at the criticism and asked for some details of the poor management, but it turned out that they were blaming Wayne for the delays in getting the IPO done when it was pretty obvious that the problem was the deterioration of the Australian and the world capital markets. It also became very obvious to us that neither of these gentlemen knew anything about the subject at hand, which was the development of a new pharmaceutical product. This was to cause continuing problems with the functioning of this board, and it gave me a particular problem. I was not used to sitting on boards with people who did not understand the business of the company. However, I finally realized that this is the Australian way and learned to ignore the worst parts of it and to continue to try to keep the company on track.

Hank and I were actually pleased with the progress that was being made at Epitan in spite of the market turmoil that was going on. Wayne had hired several well-qualified people who had created a good plan for developing the drug and were beginning to implement it. Wayne had also obtained a very nice office space on Collins Street in Melbourne at a very favorable rate because it had been vacated by a company that had recently failed. Epitan took it over on a sub-lease with no improvements needed. Even though we were a pharmaceutical company, we did not need laboratory space since all of our work was being contracted out. This resulted in considerable savings.

The main points of the plan were:

- Order over one hudnred grams of clinical-grade Melanotan-1, which we would need for clinical trials and for development of a slow release delivery product. It was quite expensive since manufacturing of peptides was still a very specialized endeavor with few companies participating. It cost us about US$1,000/gram for the drug, and it still had to be formulated into a final product, also an expensive procedure. At this stage, we were concerned about the drug costs and wondered whether we could eventually make it into a profitable commercial product. It looked to us like the drug cost might far exceed the guideline 10–20 percent of revenue, which is standard for the pharmaceutical industry. That sounds low, but the other costs of development, marketing, and product support are very high in this field.

- Meet with the Australian regulator as soon as possible, known as the Therapeutic Goods Agency, or TGA, in Canberra, to determine the regulatory route to market.
- Develop the slow-release injectable pellet and look at other forms of delivery. We still needed to increase the intensity of the tan.
- Run human trials to understand how the drug is distributed and metabolized in the body, to explore the safety of long-term use, and, when the slow release dosage form is developed, to evaluate its safety and performance in tanning.
- Review clinical indications that could be the basis of clinical trials and approval. This was the part of the plan that we felt was weakest and that we had to improve, but our thinking at this time was to focus on an indication to protect against serious sunburn damage and to leave skin cancer prevention until later. We felt that the sun damage prevention indication could be a relatively fast way to market. In contrast, an indication in skin cancer prevention would be a prolonged series of trials since, unlike sunburn, skin cancers did not arise quickly but took many years to become evident.

The rest of the board meeting was taken up with administrative, governance, and budget matters. For example, we approved a board stock trading policy, stock options for the new management, a PR policy, and agreed to search for a new chairman, among many other things. We also identified a potential serious problem with the pending expiration of the key patents and set out a plan to try to extend them and to watch for anything in our work that was surprising and could give us the basis for new patent coverage.

Patents can be very difficult to obtain and are very expensive to maintain with each country charging annual maintenance fees, so in this business, you try to only patent what is potentially very valuable and worth protecting. At this time, the worldwide patent law was in process of changing from giving seventeen years monopoly after the grant of a patent, which usually takes three to seven years from the original filing, to twenty years monopoly from the filing. Either way, since it takes about ten years to get a drug approved from first synthesis to regulatory approval to sell, there is only about seven to ten years maximum left for patent life. This means that if you can find something innovative to file a new patent somewhere in the clinical trial process, then you had a leg up on patent life. But it is not easy to find something like that since patent law does not allow a patent to be issued that has any element of obviousness about it; it must be new and non-obvious, and so, at this time, we were looking at only having a few years of life after getting approval to sell unless we could find something new to patent. As we will relate later, we had a very positive development in this area that enabled new coverage for twenty years of the slow-release formulation. But at this time, we did not know that, and this was a big concern. We finished the board meeting with all the board members being on good terms and with the little storm that we had at dinner now behind us. But I was concerned that there were some things going on that could cause problems later.

The transition of the company to Australia was now complete, and we were funded for a couple of years. Wayne had done an outstanding job, and it was now up to us to help to guide the company through the drug development process.

## Postscript to Chapter 6

As I write this postscript, on October 9, 2019, the Melanotan-1 drug was approved in the USA by the FDA yesterday for treatment of Erythropoetic Protoporphyria, or EPP, an orphan indication. It therefore gets an automatic seven years exclusivity under the Orphan Drug Act that runs parallel with the remaining patent life. Here is the FDA's news release:

> *FDA APPROVES FIRST TREATMENT TO INCREASE PAIN-FREE LIGHT EXPOSURE IN PATIENTS WITH A RARE DISORDER*
>
> ***For Immediate Release:***
> *October 08, 2019*
>
> *The U.S. Food and Drug Administration today granted approval to Scenesse (afamelanotide) to increase pain-free light exposure in adult patients with a history of phototoxic reactions (damage to skin) from erythropoietic protoporphyria.*

*For patients who are suffering from erythropoietic protoporphyria, a rare disorder, exposure to light may be extremely painful. Prior to today's approval, there were no FDA-approved treatments to help erythropoietic protoporphyria patients increase their light exposure," said Julie Beitz, M.D., director of FDA's Center for Drug Evaluation and Research Office of Drug Evaluation III. "Today's approval is one example of the FDA's ongoing commitment to encourage industry innovation of therapies to treat rare diseases, and work with drug developers to make promising new therapies available to patients as safely and efficiently as possible."*

*Erythropoietic protoporphyria is a rare disorder caused by mutations leading to impaired activity of ferrochelatase, an enzyme involved in heme production. Heme is an important component in hemoglobin, the oxygen carrying molecule in red blood cells. The decrease in ferrochelatase activity leads to an accumulation of protoporphyrin IX (PPIX) in the body. Light reaching the skin can react with PPIX causing intense skin pain and skin changes, such as redness and thickening. Scenesse (afamelanotide), a melanocortin-1 receptor (MC1-R) agonist, increases the production of eumelanin in the skin independent of exposure to sunlight or artificial light sources. It is an implant that is administered subcutaneously (inserted under the skin).*

*The efficacy of Scenesse was established in two parallel group clinical trials with patients with erythropoietic protoporphyria who received Scenesse or placebo form of the implant subcutaneously every two months. The first clinical trial enrolled 93 subjects, of whom 48 received Scenesse, and were followed for 180 days. The primary endpoint was the total number of hours over 180 days spent in direct sunlight between 10 A.M. and 6 P.M. on days with no pain. The median total number of hours over 180 days spent in direct sunlight between 10 A.M. and 6 P.M. on days with no pain was 64 hours for patients receiving Scenesse and 41 hours for patients taking placebo.*

*The second clinical trial enrolled 74 patients, of whom 38 received Scenesse, and were followed for 270 days. The primary endpoint was the total number of hours over 270 days spent outdoors between 10 am and 3 pm on days with no pain for which "most of the day" was spent in direct sunlight. The analysis did not include sun exposure on days patients reported spending time in a combination of both direct sunlight and shade. The median total number of hours over 270 days spent outdoors between 10 am and 3 pm on days with no pain for which "most of the day" was spent in direct sunlight was six hours for patients receiving Scenesse and 0.75 hours for patients receiving placebo.*

*Scenesse's most common side effects are implant site reaction, nausea, oropharyngeal (part of the throat just behind the mouth, where the oral cavity starts) pain, cough, fatigue, skin hyperpigmentation, dizziness, melanocytic nevus (moles), respiratory tract infection, somnolence (feeling drowsy), non-acute porphyria (build-up of normally occurring molecules created during heme production) and skin irritation. Scenesse should be administered by a health care professional who is proficient in the subcutaneous implantation procedure and has completed the applicant-provided training. Scenesse may induce skin darkening, and a full body skin examination is recommended for patients twice a year. In addition, patients are encouraged to maintain sun protection measures during treatment with Scenesse to prevent phototoxic reactions related to erythropoietic protoporphyria.*

*The FDA granted this application Priority Review designation. Scenesse also received Orphan Drug designation, which provides incentives to assist and encourage the development of drugs for rare diseases. The approval of Scenesse was granted to Clinuvel.*

*The FDA, an agency within the U.S. Department of Health and Human Services, protects the public health by assuring the safety, effectiveness, and security of human and veterinary drugs, vaccines and other biological products for human use, and medical devices. The agency also is responsible for the safety and security of our nation's food supply, cosmetics, dietary supplements, products that give off electronic radiation, and for regulating tobacco products.*

###

We will explain the background behind the approval in the coming chapters.

Clinuvel's stock (the successor to Epitan) has risen to A$45/share, although several reverse stock splits make it not comparable to the original Epitan shares. It has since fallen back into about the A$20–25 range. Since Scenesse was approved in the EU in 2014, this now means that it has approval in the two major world markets, and the future looks bright. However, those of us who were the founders back in the '90s are wondering why it took so long and why it is only approved for a micro-sized market.

This is actually the second one of the drug class known as the melanocortins, which were originally synthesized at the University of Arizona, to be approved in the USA. The first one to be approved, related to Melanotan-2, is known as Vyleesi, from AMAG Pharmaceuticals, and it was approved in June 2019 for female sexual dysfunction and was launched in the USA in September 2019. It is commonly known as the female Viagra.

The third application, weight loss using setmelanotide, from Rhythm Pharmaceuticals, was approved by the FDA in November of 2020. Setmelanotide is a molecule related to Melanotan-2. Rhythm has developed an impressive strategy to use these molecules in up to six orphan diseases in children who have various genetic defects which cause them to massively overeat, with devastating consequences.

If you remember the side effects of these Melanotan-2 drugs, the cyclic peptides that cross the blood/brain barrier, then these two strategies for sexual and weight-loss indications are ingenious since they avoid the problems of the multiple side effects that Hank warned us about in the early days. The female sexual indication is an acute indication with side effects that are unlikely to be a problem in such a short term, occasional use indication, and the pediatric weight-loss indications address diseases that are so serious that these side effects will likely be tolerated if the drug saves the patient's life.

It is worth noting that the female sexual indication had a serious false start when the product was developed to be administered as a nasal spray. This meant it was all in the bloodstream very quickly, and it caused unacceptable blood pressure increases, so nasal delivery had to be abandoned. Only when a slightly different version of the drug was developed in a subcutaneous single injection, where the drug is released more slowly, were the side effects more manageable.

We do, of course, look back with some anguish that we weren't smart enough to figure out these indications and strategies in the early days and that we had to give up the sexual and weight-loss indications in order to focus on tanning. Unfortunately, pharmaceutical development is like that, and you can't do everything. You are also subject to the cycles of the capital markets, and at the time, it simply was not possible to raise enough money to do all of these three major indications. However, we salute the scientists at the University of Arizona for their pioneering work in conceptualizing the analogues of melanocyte stimulating hormone to be used as drugs. They have made a major contribution to science and to alleviating suffering for many patients.

# Chapter 7
## *The First Australian Shareholder Meeting*

*Terry and Hank are introduced to the rough and tumble of the ASX.*

In the next six months, we had four telephone board meetings, and Hank and I were generally pleased with progress. The first meeting with the Australian food and drug regulator, the TGA, was held in person in May 2001, and the team was very happy with the outcome. Bob Dorr traveled specially to Australia to participate in this meeting and added a lot of credibility. The TGA appeared to be genuinely interested in what we were doing and were not putting any obvious roadblocks in our way. We got the allowance to proceed with the human clinical work outlined in the last chapter, starting in September, and we got very good co-operation at the Royal Adelaide Hospital to do the work.

In addition, we were able to order the large amount of MT-1 that we needed for the trials and to initiate the work on the development of the slow-release formulation. We decided to work with a US company to develop the slow-release pellet since they had a lot of experience in this field and could also make it commercially for us once the development was complete. However, developing this formulation proved to be a much more difficult proposition than we had planned for, and it took a lot longer and cost a lot more than we had expected. We also got an education in slow-release dosage development, which was a bit of a cold shower. But, nonetheless, we decided to continue the work, and we all felt that it would turn out to be a big improvement over the single-dose delivery. None of us foresaw the magnitude of the advance that this would prove to be nor how it would give us totally new and impregnable intellectual property for over twenty years. More on this later.

Our second in-person board meeting was scheduled for October 2001 to coincide with the company's first annual shareholder meeting. Wayne requested that we arrive early for the board meeting, which preceded the annual meeting. I was surprised when Wayne called a telephone board meeting two weeks before we left for Australia and announced that the chairman had resigned. We quickly appointed Wayne as chairman and agreed to start a search for a new chairman.

The resignation of the chairman was a surprise, but I quickly learned that it was quite normal in Australia for the chairman of a small company to move on after it was ASX-listed. As an aside, the business governance culture in Australia is to separate the roles of chairman and CEO, a situation I applauded since it guarded against the CEO becoming all powerful in a company. Further, the culture was to have a chairman who was very experienced in business and could focus on the strategic issues facing the company.

This was the time immediately after the September 11 attacks on the World Trade Center in New York, and flying then was a bit of a nervous proposition since we expected more attacks, and every flight was a nail-biting experience, especially the very long-haul flights, like our sixteen-hour endurance test flying to Australia. Every time we got off the plane at our destination, we gave thanks that we were still alive. My situation was relatively easy, since it was only a one-hour flight from Phoenix to Los Angeles to pick up the nonstop flight to Melbourne, Australia. However, Hank had to come from Philadelphia, which was a full six hours to Los Angeles, making a total of twenty-two hours of flying. However, he did not complain, and we were both excited by the progress we were making with the company.

At the in-person board meeting on October 22, 2001, we spent a long time going over the things that were to be discussed and approved at the annual meeting, which was choreographed in some detail with each board member having a role to introduce and propose certain resolutions. I ended up with the task of proposing and seeking approval for the grant of stock options for management and board, which is normally a simple process with US public companies. Little did I know that this would be the most contentious issue. I was sucked into a vortex that was difficult to navigate.

Company annual meetings in the United States are rarely a big deal for small start-up companies, even for those that are public. The annual meeting is held because the law so requires, but it is a formality, and it is unusual for shareholders to attend. Management generally regards the meeting as a nuisance since there is nobody there to listen to a presentation nor to ask questions. But we quickly learned that the annual meeting in Australia is a big deal. They usually occur in October or November, and a lot of people attend. In the discussion of these motions at the board meeting, I learned that all stock option grants have to be approved by the shareholders and that the strike price of the options granted has to be a minimum of about 30 percent above the current price of the stock, with performance milestones attached to each grant. This is a big difference from United States where options are granted in a public company at the price of the stock at the close of business on the day of the grant, and the individual options do not have to be separately approved by the shareholders

We went straight from the board meeting into the annual meeting, which was held in one of the big hotels in central Melbourne, and it appeared that there were at least six other company annual meetings going on in the same hotel at the same time. When we entered the room, there were about forty people there, most of them shareholders who were being carefully checked at the door. I was introduced to a lot of our shareholders.

Everything was fine until we got to the motions for shareholder approval, and I was asked to speak on the motion to grant stock options to board members and some of our management. I thought this was a no-brainer based upon my experience with US companies, and I was totally unprepared for the resistance that came forth from some of the shareholders. It was led by a very experienced shareholder and a formidable adversary. I have since got to know him better, since he is a fellow golfer and we met accidentally in Scotland. I hold him in high regard.

He argued very impressively that stock options should only be given as a reward for accomplishments, and so far, the board had only given losses to the shareholders with the stock mired at a very low price. I recovered quickly from my surprise and argued that stock options are meant to be an incentive as well as a reward. In the US, they are usually granted under an incentive stock option plan. Further, the board has been working for nothing up to now, and stock options would be the main compensation. Does he expect the board to work for nothing?

We went back and forth in this way for several cycles, like we were in a university debating society event. But there was no winner of this debate. Both of us had strongly held positions which were eloquently presented, but finally, Wayne, as chairman, stepped in and suggested that we defer a decision until the board could present a more detailed proposal including some milestones for the vesting of the stock options. This was agreeable to everyone, and so, we scheduled another shareholder meeting for the end of November, at which the stock options were approved. This was my baptism into the Australian way of corporate governance and especially stock option grants.

Our next in-person board meeting was scheduled for March 2002 in Melbourne. We had several phone meetings before that and were very pleased with the progress on the trial and slow-release programs, the search for new board members, and also a search for other products that we could possibly license-in to generate some revenue. But the latter search was difficult, and we came up dry. At the meeting, we heard about the results of our first small clinical trial in humans at the Royal Adelaide Hospital. Those results showed a statistically significant increase in melanin content of the skin, which was encouraging. It is all very well to see an increase in tanning, but it could be due to other factors changing the color of the skin, such as Addison's disease or simple sun exposure. The proof that it was a drug-induced increase in melanin, the natural pigment, was very reassuring and was further evidence that we were inducing a natural tan.

We also welcomed another member of the board of directors at this meeting, a dermatologist based in Melbourne who brought a very practical perspective about our product from the dermatologist's point of view. The board was now back up to strength at five members, and we were still looking to add an independent chairman. Throughout my experience on the more than twenty boards I served on as a venture capitalist, I found that the optimum board size is about five or six people. Beyond that it becomes difficult to manage the board and for each member to make a meaningful contribution.

Wayne was a member of the Melbourne Club on Collins Street, close to the Epitan offices. We held our board dinners at the Club, and some of us were even able to stay in their accommodations. The Club was an outstanding institution very much in the old English style. One amusing "tradition," although not dating back very far, was that they banned the use of mobile phones in the Club, and to enforce it, any member who had their mobile phone actually ring with an incoming call that was heard had to buy a round of drinks for everyone in the Club at the time. I witnessed one of these infractions, and the moment the ring was heard, everyone rushed for the bar in a stampede that I have not seen the like of before or since!

An amusing sidelight is that we decided to create a company internet website. These were quite new at the time, and nobody was quite sure how useful they would be. We were amazed that people seemed to be able to find our website, and we were inundated with responses to our invitation for the name of the website visitor and for them to indicate whether they would be interested in participating in our clinical trials of tanning. Just about everybody who filled out this response indicated they would be interested to participate in the trials, and we got many thousands of names. This also led us to look into how many tanning salons there are in United States, and we were shocked to learn that there were about 6,500 salons. This seemed to be a very good proxy for the market size of our MT-1 product for cosmetic uses. Although we had not yet conclusively proven the safety of MT-1, we were well on the way, and it contrasted with the well-known cancer-causing dangers of the ultraviolet light used to get a tan in a tanning salon. Yet people continued to use these salons in very high numbers, showing that they would go to great lengths to change their skin color with a tan. We felt we were riding a tiger and could probably develop a product that could have similar revenues to Botox for wrinkles. This was the beginning of the increasingly rancorous debates among board members about where we should focus: on the cosmetic tanning market or the orphan drug market. I was in the cosmetic camp, but I was to ultimately lose the argument—more about that later.

We added our sixth board member in mid-2002. This was an impressive marketing executive whom I was introduced to by my good friend Dr. Ian Gust, a world-class immunologist in Melbourne who has been one of my golfing friends in Australia and Scotland for nearly twenty years now. The new member was with Ian at CSL, a successful Australian blood products company, and he was the perfect complement to the mix of people we now had on the board.

As we approached our next in-person board meeting in Melbourne in November 2002, we were increasingly concerned about our cash level, and we started talking to the Melbourne investment banks about doing a follow-on equity raise. However, the market crash in the US following the popping of the internet bubble had created problems for fundraising, and so, we had to look to other means. As possible sources of cash, we agreed to look at getting the rights to sell some generic dermatology products in Australia and to seek a corporate partner.

At the November board meeting, we agreed that there was an opportunity to create a generic dermatology drug marketing company in Australia and that we could be well positioned to fill that role. We worked on a one-page strategy document at the board dinner and agreed that we would proceed to implement it. What amazed me was how the company proceeded to ignore the conditions that we put in the strategy document, but that didn't become evident for a while. The most important condition was that we wanted to build the opportunity on a cash-positive basis by bringing in the products first and then expanding with infrastructure later. But they did it the other way around. In brief, we spent a lot of money on the strategy, achieved nothing, and worsened our cash burn rate.

We talked to a lot of potential corporate partners, but we were not far enough along to do that kind of deal. They wanted to see more human clinical trial results and a specific medical application that we could go to market with.

The clinical program was focused on confirming the results of the UA studies and optimizing the dose in case we had to go with the series of single daily injections. We added a second hospital, the Royal Alfred in Sydney, as a clinical trial site, and we wanted to add two or three other clinical sites to bring us up to the number needed to expeditiously complete the trial program. Sites in Brisbane and Adelaide were close to opening.

As it turned out, the most important work we were doing at this time was the development of the controlled release product, but we did not realize it at the time. We were building on the initial work done at UA, and we were working with a company in the USA that specialized in developing these kinds of products. Work was started at the end of 2001, and it was now getting to the point where we had a formulation that released slowly over about ten days. We were close to the initial trials of this formulation in animals, which were necessary before we could use it in humans.

So, by the end of the 2002 year, we were making good progress on the clinical program, and we had added two good board members and several members of the management team, including a CFO and a business development executive. Our main concern was funding, and we felt we had that under control either from internally generated sources if we could create a generic dermatology business, or from a capital raise with our friendly investment bankers. But the storm clouds after the collapse of the Internet bubble were still hanging over the financing market, and we were becoming increasingly concerned.

# Chapter 8
## *Breakthrough! The controlled release formulation*

*Terry relates the thrilling story of releasing the drug slowly over several days.*

There were three priorities for Epitan in 2003: raise more money, raise more money, and raise more money! Seriously, the funding situation was dire, and that's the way it seemed. Actually, the other two priorities were to get the human results of the controlled release product and to find a clinical indication that we could use to get the product approved and on the market. Taking these in turn:

**Funding.** We were able to raise about A$10 million through a rights' offering to existing shareholders at a 15 percent discount to the market price. We were able to do this since the financing markets were starting to improve after the dot-com crash. Plus, the ASX had some favorable rules that help companies to raise money. However, this was not without going through a nervous time when our cash dipped down below the critical A$1million level, and we came close to implementing our emergency plan to cut expenses, which included firing some key people. We regarded ourselves as fortunate and moved on.

**Controlled release.** We completed the clinical trials with the single daily dosing schedule, and we were gratified to be getting about the same degree of tanning as in the university trials. We also confirmed that those patients with the lightest skins got the greatest amount of skin tanning change, which was very encouraging. However, the liquid formulation needed at least fifteen days of subcutaneous doses, and we were still getting the side effects of transient, or short-lived, nausea and flushing in some of the patients. This was not ideal, but we could have proceeded with it if necessary. All of us were hoping that the controlled-release formulation would give better results.

Progress on the controlled-release product was slower than we expected, but we finally selected a formulation, completed the animal studies with no complications, and we were ready to treat the first humans in November 2003.

The controlled-release product consisted of the dose of the active peptide, MT-1, dispersed in a special biocompatible slow dissolving material. This was made into the form of a small cylindrical pellet about a half inch long and a tenth of an inch in diameter. It was injected with a special device into the flesh of the underside of the patient's forearm from where it slowly dissolved and released the dose over about ten days. The slow-dissolving matrix material had been developed many years ago and was already proven to be safe which made the regulatory situation much easier. Throughout this process, the Australian "FDA," known as the TGA, was very helpful and cooperative.

The controlled-release clinical study was an accelerating dose study in healthy volunteers in Australia, and we started with what we thought was the minimum dose that would not show any tanning. This was about the same dose as used in the single injections, and we reasoned that since it was released over at least ten days, then the average amount per day would be about 10 percent of the single daily dose that we already knew, from the university's dose escalation trial, did not cause any detectable tanning. Then we would escalate the dose from there until we got the desired amount of tanning.

Soon after the first dosing, I got the phone call from Wayne in December 2003 that is described in chapter one. We were all dumbfounded that this low dose was enough to induce such a significant amount of tanning, much greater than the much higher cumulative single daily doses. The reason was possibly that activating the receptors continuously, even at this low level, had a much greater effect than the larger amount of drug being injected all at once. Because of the short half-life of the peptide in blood, most of the drug given by a single-dose injection was gone in less than two hours. And the added bonus, a big one, was that there were none of the side effects that were seen with the single daily doses. In summary, there were four major advantages of the increased safety and efficacy of the controlled-release dose:

1. A much deeper tan, or higher efficacy, at a lower total dose. This made the drug a true commercial proposition.
2. Elimination of most of the side effects. This would make the situation with the regulators much easier and make the drug more commercially viable

3. By needing less peptide per dose, the slow release formulation allowed for a much more attractive gross margin, in line with a typical pharmaceutical target level of 80 percent or more. Gross margin is the difference between the selling price and the cost to make the dose of the drug, expressed as a percentage of the selling price. We had started to worry about the financial viability of the drug since the peptide was so expensive to manufacture. At a cost of about US$1,000 per gram, if we had to administer fifteen consecutive daily doses of about 20 mg each, the cost of the 300 mg of peptide itself would have been about US$300. Add the cost of making the controlled-release dose and the cost of goods would have been over $400/dose. But if the dose was only a total of 20 mg, then the cost of the peptide in the dose would be only about US$20, giving more pricing options and making the drug much more commercially attractive.
4. For patent purposes, since this was such a surprising result, it passed the patentability criterion of not being obvious to a person skilled in the art and allowed us to file a totally new patent that covered all types of controlled-release doses. This was a huge advantage and gave us an additional twenty years of market exclusivity under a patent monopoly.

In summary, the success of the controlled-release dosage form was a huge win for us, and we started to rethink our strategies. For the first time, I could see a clear path to building a very big company with a highly successful blockbuster drug.

**Clinical indication.** We still had not found the ideal clinical indication to use as our market entry point. We had considered and rejected many of them since most seemed to require very long duration clinical trials, for example, skin cancer prevention. For the moment, we had settled on an indication called polymorphous light eruption, or PMLE, which is the unfortunate condition where the patient is allergic to sunlight. This occurs almost exclusively in light-skinned individuals, and it was likely that tanning would effectively treat the condition. But the success of the controlled-release product caused a change in the strategic thinking of some of the board members, and we were finally thinking about going after the enormous market of cosmetic tanning that would put the tanning salons out of business. This was to be an ongoing point of disagreement among board members that would cause a significant rift in the company.

# Chapter 9

## *Different Interests*

*Terry discovers that some board members wanted to make a quick profit and move on.*

We entered 2004 in a euphoric mood. We were elated with the controlled-release results and congratulated ourselves on the development of a unique drug with outstanding patent coverage that seemed to be safe with a very high efficacy. There was just a minor problem of raising a significant amount of capital to move us forward and completing the clinical development and regulatory approval to get on the market. What could possibly go wrong? Unfortunately, the mood did not last. It was obvious that we had some significant issues inside the company, issues that blindsided most of the board.

We quickly ran more clinical trials in Australia to optimize the implant dose, learn how to finetune the implant to give it an optimal release rate, and to look at other modes of delivery, such as across the skin, to be sure that there was not an even better way to administer the drug. We also had to complete the other regulatory requirements that would enable us to perform the required clinical studies to gain approval to market the product, initially in Australia and then in the USA, Europe, and the rest of the world.

The results came in quickly, and we learned that the optimum dose was even lower than our first estimated level, further increasing the commercial viability of the drug. Finding the best controlled-release rate was a bit more difficult, but we eventually settled on slow release over about ten days. We also found that delivery across the skin did not work.

We set to work with our patent counsel to draft the new patent, which would cover all the ways of delivering the drug continuously at these low dosing levels to induce a tan. The new patent was filed by mid-2004 and gave us new patent coverage for twenty years. This was a very significant development and secured our strong intellectual property position. Normally, you need to have a composition of matter patent, covering the drug structure itself to have a really strong patent monopoly. But in this case, the slow-release efficacy was so unexpected and so unique that our new patent effectively stopped any competition until the patent expired twenty years later. Since the original patents licensed from UA were just about to expire, this was indeed fortunate and added a lot of potential value to the company. It also eliminated the necessity to pay royalties on future sales.

I had assumed that we were all dedicated to growing Epitan into a big company to maximize the shareholder returns. As a venture capitalist, this is the reason for our existence, and I thought we had worked out with the key players that this was our mission. However, several developments as 2003 ended and 2004 progressed gave me a nasty shock that others had different ideas.

Wayne and I had many conversations in the early days about growing Epitan into a significant pharmaceutical company in Australia since, to our knowledge, this had not been done with a locally developed novel drug without the involvement of a big company. The significance of not having a big company involved is that you don't have to give up value to the big company, and you can build the company to a much greater market capitalization, in other words, a high stock price. Corporate partnerships typically destroy value, they do not build it. Many entrepreneurs have learned this fact too late to do anything about it, since the funding that comes from the corporate partner comes at the price of giving up the sales and marketing function wherein most of the profitability lies.

Australia actually has quite an impressive capital market structure, including numerous investment banks, a vibrant stock exchange, and high net worth investors. There is also an Australian tradition of risk-taking, developed primarily with the mining companies, but now being extended to the life sciences arena. This made it feasible to raise funds in Australia if the conditions were right.

However, several things happened as 2003 drew to a close and 2004 unfolded that made me question whether we were all pulling in the same direction or whether the CEO and some of the other management members were looking for a quick sale of the company at the sacrifice of a longer-term, much higher value creation. These included:

1. **Some disagreements in our board and management strategy sessions.** I felt that with the outstanding controlled-release results, we now had a product that we could develop for the cosmetic tanning business, which is a huge market, probably in excess of US$2 billion per year spent in the existing tanning salons around the world. If the customers would pay a premium for tanning with ultraviolet light in the salons or on the beach, which has significant safety issues, then they would pay much more for a safe and efficacious drug. A drug which gave them a natural tan without sunlight but which they could augment with further exposure to the sun if desired. We felt that we needed a selling price below a thousand dollars for a three-month duration of dosing to have a product that would be widely used cosmetically. And now that we had significantly reduced the product cost of manufacture and delivery, we felt we could achieve that. In addition, the approval of a cosmetic application would be a much longer regulatory process, probably needing several thousand patients in a phase-three trial. Thus, it would require raising much more money. But it would give access to an extraordinarily large market and enable us to build Epitan into a large company. However, others felt we should keep to the small clinical markets that we were still trying to define. I could not understand why they did not want to go for the brass ring! If we could get the cosmetic approval, it could then be used in all of the clinical indications as well, but probably not vice versa.

2. **The CEO was selling Epitan stock.** This was a shock even though I had seen it before in companies at this stage where the management was not financially secure. It was not illegal, but it was unusual and frowned upon by investors and usually punished by a falling stock price. Wayne had sold some of his stock without consulting the board or the CFO of the company to confirm it was allowed. That is the normal route in order to determine that there is no material insider information that has not been publicly disclosed. Indeed, if stock had been sold while the seller was in possession of material undisclosed information, this would have violated Australian securities laws. The US SEC (Securities and Exchange Commission) has the same regulation.

   The first we heard about it was when we saw a news release disclosing the stock sale. It is never a good idea to surprise your board of directors, but that is precisely what happened, and predictably, this caused some problems with the Australian investors. We had a communications crisis on our hands since it gave the company a black eye and investors assumed that there was something very wrong. That caused the stock to lose significant value immediately after the required regulatory announcement of the CEO's stock sales. We had quite a mess to clean up, and Wayne had to put out a news release that it was not his intention to sell any more stock for the next six months. This seemed to satisfy the criticisms. But it made me suspicious of Wayne's intentions, and it started me thinking about getting a new CEO.

You can imagine the board's reaction when, barely three months later, Wayne's stock sales started again and, again, with no consultation with the board or the CFO. I had a very angry call with Wayne and reminded him of the news release he had issued three months ago where he said that it was not his intention to sell more stock for six months. His explanation was very simple: at the time he put out the news release, it was certainly not his intention to sell anymore stock for six months, but now his intentions had changed. I was disgusted, especially since the stock had taken another leg down on announcement of Wayne's second stock sale. We wanted to immediately terminate him, but this would have made a bad situation worse, and so, we mutually agreed that he would not renew his contract in February 2005, and we started the search for a new CEO.

3. **Management was pushing very hard to get a corporate partner.** They went off on their own and did this without consulting the board and presented us with a deal that was at an advanced stage to hire a consultant at an exorbitant fee with very large back-end payments. I was forced to lead the board resistance to doing this, and we did not approve it. But it created some bad feelings among the board and management, and it further fed my suspicions that management simply wanted to sell out and move on.

It is worth a short digression to talk about managements that want to sell out for a relatively small gain today, rather than risk going forward to build a much more valuable company. I had experienced this several times with some of our other companies in the past. And once management gets the company into the position of looking to be acquired, with a "for sale" sign on the company, it is very difficult to reverse it. The reason, of course, is that if you are not financially secure, the prospect of putting a million dollars in your bank account is very attractive, and it dominates what is perceived as the high risk of continuing to go forward and possibly losing it all. You may ask how this can happen, since all the power is vested in the board. The answer is that the board and investors need a management team to run the company, and they do not want to be suddenly faced with having to do it themselves. Therefore, management has a great deal of "soft" power which can significantly influence board members. Fear of suddenly not having the key managers to run the company can be a powerful motivator, especially if the managers already have their stock options vested. This is the reason that as I became a seasoned venture capitalist with many of these experiences, I much preferred to have financially secure CEOs running our companies. They were far more rational and could be relied upon to seek the most value-creating strategy rather than blindly going for a short-term gain.

I still bear the scars of these battles, but in the process, I picked up enough experience so that with the help of the other board members, we were able to take quick action to bring things under control at Epitan and to return the focus to building a large company, rather than a quick sell-out. But in the aftermath of our big controlled release clinical trial success, we had been badly wounded, and it seriously affected our ability to raise the capital needed to go forward.

As part of Wayne's departure package, we agreed to make him non-executive chairman for the next year, and we initiated a search for a new chairman and for at least one new board member that could help us in the fundraising. The capital markets had deteriorated again, and we were seriously worried about our ability to finance the company, especially with the stock price now so low.

Fortunately, we had a ready candidate to take over as CEO when Wayne vacated that position in February 2005. He had done a good job in hiring a chief financial officer (CFO) with an excellent pedigree, Iain Kirkwood. Although he had minimal experience in the pharmaceutical field, we had confidence in him to fill the position while we continued the CEO search.

Iain Kirkwood was an ex-pat Englishman who had been in Australia many years. He had a very solid finance and accounting background and had previously been the CFO of several public ASX companies. When we hired him at EpiTan, the board was surprised that we were able to get someone of his caliber to be our CFO since he could have commanded a much greater cash compensation package elsewhere. However, Iain was financially secure and was seeking a high upside position where he could get a significant stock option package with potential high returns. He was personable (rare for a finance type), presented well and knew a lot of the key finance and business people in the community. He gave the board confidence in his ability to manage the numbers. He also shared our strategic goal of maximizing the investor returns by building a large company in Australia without corporate partner involvement. We were all reeling from the recent onerous Sarbanes-Oxley, or SOX, regulatory legislation in the USA and expecting the same package to be passed in Australia. Thus, we needed someone of Iain's caliber to make sure we stayed out of regulatory trouble. We were not disappointed, and it was a no-brainer to make him interim CEO. The transition was made in February 2005.

We need to explain Sarbanes-Oxley (SOX) and its impact on the investing world. Around about the turn of the millennium, there were several very high-profile scandals in the USA caused by abuses of the accounting regulations. The most notorious case is that of Enron, where many people lost a lot of money and several executives were convicted and sent to jail. The US Congress responded with the SOX legislation that was passed into law with bipartisan support. SOX severely tightened the regulations surrounding the financial reporting, accounting, and auditing of public companies. It is generally recognized that this was probably an overreaction, but public companies have to live with it and similar legislation was passed in most countries that are significant to investors. Companies have learned to handle SOX, but at the time, we were all scared of it and wanted competent financial people in our companies to make sure we complied.

Wayne operated well as non-executive chairman, which was a part-time role. He had caught the venture capital bug and wanted to set up his own operation. We readily agreed to give him an office at the company for the first year while he got this going.

In September, we moved the company to a new office at 1 Collins Street, a few blocks north and on the corner of the Treasury building square. The lease had run out on the former office, and this one was available at an incredibly low rent, since the Melbourne commercial real estate market had still not recovered. It was a magnificent location, and the facilities were superb, making us look like a growing company on the move. The offices were on the fourth floor, and the main conference room was on the corner with a nice view of the old Treasury Building, which was built at the time of the gold rush in the 1850s. It always seemed to me that Melbourne had two building sprees, one after the 1850s gold rush leaving many of the superb Victorian buildings sprinkled around the city, and then another in the 1990s with high-rise glass and concrete towers. It made for a unique city.

# Chapter 10

## *Salvation from an Unlikely Source*

*Terry is pleasantly surprised by a deep-pocketed investor*

When Iain Kirkwood took over in February 2005, the company was low on cash, and his first order of business was to raise money to continue our development plan. He set about the task with gusto and quickly determined that the timing was not right to raise our A$20 million target funding in Australia. The Australian market was in sympathy with the US market and simply not receptive to funding our kind of company. With the wisdom of hindsight, we now call this period the Biotech Desert, because the very word was enough to have investors hide their checkbooks. It lasted until about 2013, when it was broken by an ebullient public market.

Iain had experience with the UK markets, and he proposed that we raise capital and list on the new AIM (Alternative Investment Market) market in London. The London Stock Exchange had recently formed this separate market for unprofitable start-up companies like us. The big innovation was that AIM was regulation-light, and they did this by delegating responsibility for the company diligence to a nominated advisor, or NOMAD, who had the legal responsibility if something later emerged that should have been found out during the diligence investigations. This significantly shortened and decreased the cost of the fundraising process, although there was still a lot of paperwork and you became very close to your NOMAD.

We selected a NOMAD in March, and the process went along much faster than a typical American NASDAQ public offering. We had an in-person board meeting in Melbourne where the board was questioned by and got to know the NOMAD representatives over a two-day intensive session. Conducting this process from half a world away was interesting, to say the least, and involved a lot of travel between London and Melbourne, with some stops in the USA, but we somehow kept it moving. However, in May, just before we were going to initiate the offering, there was a downturn in the London market, and we were not able to get it done. So, we were still left with the problem of raising money, and now the problem was becoming acute. We had no alternative but to raise additional capital by taking advantage of the ASX regulation that allowed the sale of new shares not to exceed 15 percent of the current total share number, at a discount to the market price. This was known as a right's offering. With the stock price so low, this resulted in considerable dilution, but it kept us going.

During the AIM diligence process, we had continued our search for a sixth board member using a local headhunter, and at the end of April, we selected a candidate, just in time for him to experience the failed AIM offering. He joined the board on the understanding that he would take over as executive chairman in a few months if he proved to be compatible with the board. This would mean, of course, that Wayne would step down from the chairman role, which was fine with him, although he wanted to stay on the board.

The new member was a PhD who had experience with two large pharmaceutical companies before he took up an entrepreneurial career running several start-up drug development companies. He understood what we were trying to do, had been in the fundraising wars before, and was a great help going forward. We now had myself and Hank as the American representatives on the board, Iain as CEO and board member, Wayne as non-executive chairman, plus marketing and development executives from the pharmaceutical business. It was a compatible board and functioned well at this difficult time.

Nothing concentrates the minds of the board and management as well as the prospect of running out of money. This caused an intensive review of our strategy and a focus on how to cut expenses. We finally axed the effort to set up a generic drug marketing operation—we had looked at several opportunities, but all required significant capital outlays, and most needed regulatory work, and so, it was never going to be a source of cash for us. We also terminated our efforts to start the regulatory approval process for Melanotan in the USA—we had engaged some people in the USA as consultants, and we were writing an IND (investigational new drug application) to start PMLE (polymorphous light eruption, or "sun allergy") trials there. But with capital short, this was too expensive for us to continue, so we restricted our clinical trial efforts to Australia and the EU. We also parted with our in-house clinical trials manager and appointed Hank as our CSO (chief scientific officer). This was a role that he was very well qualified to perform, and we were delighted that he was willing to take it on, even though he was in his late sixties and lived in Philadelphia, Pennsylvania. But work was Hank's pleasure; he didn't need the money but wanted to see Melanotan come to market. We never regretted this decision.

The rights offering had only raised about A$3 million, and we still needed to raise at least A$20 million. While we were worrying about how to do this, funding materialized from a surprising source. During the many trips to London and other European centers in pursuit of the AIM offering, the management team had been introduced to numerous potential investors, including a German hedge fund manager named Florian Homm. We did not take him seriously at first, since hedge funds are rarely interested in unprofitable start-up companies, and we naturally concluded that when he found out that we were still a long way from generating revenues, his interest would evaporate. But this was no ordinary hedge fund mogul!

Florian was very tall and athletic. In his youth, he had played basketball at an international level, and he brought that kind of energy to everything that he did. He definitely had "presence" and was the focus of attention in a room full of people. He had started the hedge fund in Germany but then moved the operation to Mallorca in the Spanish Balearic Islands. He had an eclectic portfolio of investments, including ownership of one of the big German football teams. He still did business in the traditional way with jacket, shirt and tie. He was well dressed, presented well, and had the short attention span that is characteristic of the hedge fund breed. He is one of the most interesting people that I have ever met.

Florian's interest in Epitan arose from the essay he wrote during his MBA studies at Harvard speculating on how humans could use the ability to change their skin color. At the time, tanning was only possible through sun exposure. With Epitan, he had come to the right place, and after his thorough diligence, he seemed to be very interested, although he was critical of the way we had handled the development program. He made a small investment later in 2005 with a much larger amount conditioned on a company restructuring that included installing a new CEO and making board changes. We were receptive to his proposal and started to work out the details.

This all started to take shape in July 2005, and Florian had a CEO candidate in mind. It so happened that I was in London at the time, returning from The Open golf event in St. Andrews, and was able to arrange a hasty meeting with his candidate, Philippe Wolgen, MD, at London airport. Philippe was from Belgium, was trained as a surgeon, had just graduated with his MBA, and was looking for a company to run. We got on well, even though he did not like my comments about MBA's running companies. But after he met the rest of the board, we agreed that we would add him to the board of directors. Then if, after a few months, things were going well, he would take over as CEO. So, Philippe joined the board in August 2005. At the same time, Wayne stepped down as chairman, and we appointed an executive chairman.

In the next few months, the deal with Florian started to take shape. The main thing we had in common was that we both saw the tremendous potential of the Melanotan drug as the basis for building a very large company. Where we differed was that he saw it as a way to darken your skin to prevent skin cancer and fix other skin problems and wanted to get it approved in the various medical indications. I felt that we should focus on the cosmetic market since the regulators would not allow the off-label use that has led to the rise of Botox. And if we got cosmetic approval, then it would be available to be prescribed (but not *officially* promoted), for all the other medical indications, without separate approvals. But doing it his way would limit it to the medical indication that was approved and would involve separate trials for all the indications, a time-consuming and expensive strategy (as it has turned out to be). He did not know the pharma business and the bureaucracy of the regulators.

We had numerous meetings to work out the details of his investment, primarily in London, and I started to build a great deal of respect for Florian. He was not a micro manager, but he knew what he wanted, and he expected Philippe to come in as CEO to revitalize the company and devise a plan to get the drug to market. He was happy to delegate just about everything to the CEO, and he would raise the capital to implement the plan, if he was satisfied with it. He was as good as his word. Philippe took over as CEO in November 2005 with an investment from Florian and the prospect that he would raise a lot more capital if he liked the new plan.

This suited me well since I had been retired from the venture capital business since 2003. But you never really retire as a VC, and there are always some of your old companies that require your attention. In addition to Epitan, I had taken on the CEO/chairman role at one of our other companies, Vital Therapies (VTL), in San Diego, California, which was developing a cellular therapy for liver failure. This was supposed to be just a six-month interim CEO role, but it was turning into much more than that. VTL had been invited into China by the Chinese FDA and some of their leading liver docs because they thought we had the solution to liver failure from hepatitis B infection that kills over four hundred thousand people per year in China. We were now in the middle of running a pivotal clinical trial on our product at two hospitals in Beijing, and it was consuming much of my time (the next book will share this story). I was therefore somewhat stretched and traveling all the time between Scottsdale, San Diego, Beijing, and Melbourne. Therefore, if Epitan were well managed and financed, I would welcome the opportunity to step down from the board to focus all of my time on VTL. I could also sense that I was the target of a lot of criticism, much of it justified, about the slow development progress and other problems of Epitan. Thus, I felt that the new regime would probably be glad to be rid of me. However, I committed to stay around to help as needed while Phillippe completed his review and restructuring.

In November 2006, the news came in that Florian had been shot in the chest during a robbery in Caracas, Venezuela. The story is that he was shot when he gave up his wallet but refused to hand over his Rolex. It sounded bad, but Florian was extraordinarily lucky—the bullet had missed all of his major blood vessels and lodged close to the heart. He recovered quickly. We were dealing with a man who got involved with some strange situations, and I wondered what else might happen.

I can't leave the subject of Florian without mentioning his book *Rogue Financier*, which was published in 2013. It is the story of his life, and what a story it is. We did not know his background when we did business with him in 2005, but I urge the reader to get a copy and read it—there is never a dull moment, and it is really informative and educational. Clinuvel gets a mention along with a hefty dose of criticism of the board and management prior to his coming on board. The criticism is valid, but we had to deal with a very different financial and business climate, and we had limited funds available to move things forward. The story of his exit from his hedge fund is extraordinary.

In early 2006, Florian's fund invested about A$10 million, and Philippe started to analyze and restructure EpiTan.

# Chapter 11

## *Restructuring. Epitan Morphs into Clinuvel*

*Terry learns how fundraising should be done!*

As 2006 got underway and Philippe started his analysis and creation of a new business plan, I was expecting to be asked to step down from the board any day, but it did not happen. Surprisingly, even though Philippe and I had many differences, we seemed to get along because we shared an excitement about getting this drug to market. He impressed me with his attention to detail and obvious strategic mind, and I was probably useful to him with my legacy knowledge of the events that got us to this point and experience of sitting on the boards of over twenty start-ups. We struck up a good working relationship, and he used to tease me about the liver company, calling it the "foie gras" company. I shot back about MBAs not knowing how to run companies. It was all good natured. We both had a good sense of humor and shared a love of old English cars. Mine was Rolls/Bentley, and his was Jaguar.

We disagreed about several things, but the main points were:

1. I wanted to go after the large tanning markets, such as cosmetic, sun allergy, and cancer prevention, and he wanted to attack the small niche orphan markets, in the same way that Botox entered the market which is described in chapter four.
2. He favored having business generalists added to the board, and I wanted to add experienced pharmaceutical people. This was a key point of conflict, and it has ended up with today's board having no member that has experience in the pharmaceutical business. The reader can judge the results.

Even though I disagreed with Philippe's strategy, I gave in on both points since he was going to have to run the company long after I ceased to be around.

A continuing problem was that we had been unable to identify a small niche orphan market that made sense in spite of doing a lot of work on the subject. This inspired him, and he used his physician knowledge to dig deeply into these potential markets. I was very impressed with the work that he did, and he finally proposed that we focus on a rare genetic disease called erythro-poetic protoporphyria, or EPP. There are several types of porphyrias, since this is a disease caused by the body's incorrect synthesis of hemoglobin, the substance which carries oxygen and makes blood red. There can be defects at many points along the complicated hemoglobin biosynthesis pathway. In EPP, the defect is in the last step of synthesis by an enzyme called ferrochelatase. That defect causes the build-up of an intermediate type of porphyrin in the bloodstream. Unfortunately, that misformed hemoglobin intermediate is activated to a toxic form when exposed to light through the skin. That meant that EPP subjects became exquisitely photosensitive, such that victims suffered severe pain on exposure to the sun, often measured at ten on the one-to-ten pain scale. Over time, EPP patients developed blisters and permanently scarred skin. As a result, they could not go out in daylight and lived reclusive lives, needing extreme coverup of any sun exposed areas in daylight.

Since the FDA defines an orphan disease as one which affects less than two hundred thousand people per year, EPP easily qualifies since there are only about five thousand people in the world suffering from this genetic defect. The EPP patients were mostly in geographic clusters since it was passed on from the victim's parents. One such cluster was around Zürich in Switzerland, and Philippe took me to meet with a physician at Tremli Hospital in Zurich who treated this cluster of EPP patients. She was very impressive and encouraged us to pursue this since it would be a significant improvement in the lives of these patients, and it was reasonable to expect that inducing a tan would allow them to go out in the daylight. She was very interested in participating in our clinical trials. So, we now had a viable indication to focus on, and Philippe could finish his restructuring plan. Florian was delighted with the plan and encouraged us to go forward. These were the major points of the plan:

1. Continue to perfect the controlled-release delivery system and make sure the patent protection was strong.

2. Switch the main clinical indication of the trials to EPP but keep the existing PMLE trial running and begin to plan for a trial in skin cancer prevention in transplant patients. These were regarded as back-up indications if for some reason EPP had problems.
3. Focus on approval in EU as the first market.
4. Change the name of the company to Clinuvel to better reflect the clinical nature of the company. Also change the logo to a fearsome-looking Australian frilled lizard that represented our spirit.
5. Implement a plan to be on the market in three years in the EU and then use the data to gain approval in USA two years later (from 2006, it actually took nine years to get EU approval and thirteen years to get US FDA approval).
6. Add additional orphan indication approvals in our main markets.
7. Raise A$60 million to implement the plan.

The board approved the plan in April 2006, and Florian offered to host fundraising presentations in Europe as soon as we were ready. Then came another surprise. Philippe asked me to help in the drafting of the presentations and to take the lead as the first speaker in the investor meetings. Since I was expecting to be asked to step down, I was surprised, but I agreed to work with him on the fundraising. We spent a lot of time in drafting sessions debating each slide, but it was all very constructive and resulted in a very good presentation. We were ready to meet with investors in a few weeks and set up a road trip to Frankfurt and Mannheim in Germany and then Zurich in Switzerland in May 2006. Florian joined us at each meeting.

I was expecting that Florian would hire an investment bank to do the fundraising and set up the meetings, but he did it all himself. The audiences were high net-worth individual investors who followed him into his deals. I was very impressed since this was not an investor group that I had experience dealing with. They were very interesting people. I was not sure of Philippe's fundraising strategy until we went through the first investor meeting. The format was that Florian introduced us and the company, I gave the main presentation, and then Philippe spoke last. He used his time to describe all the risks and detailed why it probably would not work, leaving the question of if it did work to be answered in the listener's mind. Frankly, it was a brilliant strategy and led to very successful fundraising. Investors had never encountered a company like Clinuvel, one that spent time emphasizing the risks. Rather, they were used to CEOs always accentuating the upside to which they had to apply an appropriate discount factor, and then they had to decide whether to invest. This was different, and they were appreciative of the candor. We finished off this three-city road show at the Baur au Lac Hotel in Zurich, and by the end of that day, we had firm subscriptions for our targeted A$25 million. I was amazed at how fast it came together and even more amazed when Philippe closed the deal in two weeks with the funds in the bank. Then I departed for some golf at St. Andrews in Scotland. After all, I was supposed to be retired!

The rest of 2006 was a time of implementation of the plan for Philippe mixed with several fundraising meetings, mostly in London and Zurich. I accompanied Philippe on most of these trips. I was able to fit these in between my commuting to China to take care of numerous clinical trials and other issues for the "foie gras" company, Vital Therapies.

After a very productive Clinuvel road show in Zurich in September, we decided to raise an additional A$25 million, which was underwritten by Florian. This turned out to be over-subscribed, and we actually closed on A$35 million in November making a total of A$60 million raised, as set out in the plan.

Clinuvel was now very well financed thanks to Florian's masterful fundraising and Philippe's unique presentation strategy.

Philippe was able to get a small phase-two trial in EPP patients completed in early 2007 in Switzerland with the Zurich patient cluster. Twelve EPP patients were enrolled, and each acted as their own control with the end point measured by the amount of time they could tolerate outside, in the sun. Taking an arbitrary time as the end point, we actually got statistical significance in these twelve patients, which was amazing. So, now we knew that it was effective in EPP, we started to design a phase-three trial in EPP with about ninety patients.

As an aside, 2006 was the year of the football world cup held in Germany, and most of us were fans of our national teams, including me, Philippe, and Florian, so there was a lot of amusing banter about the good German and Belgian teams and the lousy English and USA teams (or so the Germans said—which was confirmed by the results!). There was too much going on with my two active companies for me to be in Germany for any of the matches, but I made sure to watch as many as possible on TV. The final between France and Italy was on the date of a Clinuvel board meeting in July, and I found myself watching this very controversial final in my hotel room in Australia at a most uncivilized time and in the depth of winter in Melbourne, since the seasons are reversed in the southern hemisphere.

In November of 2006, Mac Hadley, one of the three founders of Melanotan, was murdered in a home robbery at his home in Tucson. This was a shock to all of us, and the world lost a unique and effective scientist. Bob relates the story in the next chapter.

# Chapter 12

## *The Life and Death of Mac Hadley*

*Bob writes a eulogy to his very good friend, Mac*

I first met Professor Mac Hadley purely by chance one day on the sixth floor of the University of Arizona's University Hospital. That sixth floor was the Internal Medicine floor wherein one wing housed the inpatient medicine wards, including the medical ICU, and the other wing provided offices, conference rooms, and outpatient clinics for the Department of Medicine. I had just left the Hematology/Oncology Section faculty offices and heard my name called from the other side of the hallway. It was Norman (Norm) Levine, MD, then head of the dermatology section of Internal Medicine. In his office, Norm introduced me to Mac, who immediately launched into a mind-numbing description of the white powder in the vial in his hand—Nle4-D-Phe7-α-MSH, now known as afamelanotide and also as MT-1. After years of studying peptide derivatives of α-MSH in his lab on the main campus, Mac's basic science group had selected that molecule as the prime candidate for testing in humans, something he wanted Norm to immediately undertake as the head of dermatology. Hence, he had brought over a vial of the drug for Norm to administer to human volunteers.

I instantly knew why Norm had called me, as it was abundantly clear that Professor Hadley had no inkling of how drugs actually came to be tested in humans and the complexity of the preclinical development that had to occur before any molecule could be legally and safely administered to a human subject for the first time. I tried not to act too shocked, and hoped I didn't seem off-putting, but calmly stated that there were many steps that would be needed (like typically several millions of dollars invested and years of chemistry, formulation toxicology, all to FDA standards and review). But I didn't say it couldn't be done. And I promised that I would try to get "up to speed" with Mac's work, which was mainly based on frog skin bioassays to determine the potency of the many (fifty-plus) different α-MSH peptide analogs coming from Victor Hruby's chemistry lab.

Getting up to speed subsequently entailed a tour of Mac's lab, seeing the *Rana Pipiens* Northern Tree Frogs, and getting to meet Victor Hruby and his all-important chemistry graduate students who were synthesizing these molecules with prodigious output. I learned that Mac had tested some of these peptides in every type of species he could find, including lizards and rattlesnakes, yes, rattlesnakes, that he had personally collected from forays into the Sonoran Desert areas west of Tucson, and sometimes right in his own westside neighborhood. Mac also gave me a copy of his signature book *Endocrinology*, and it became clear that he was a world leader in the basic science and biology of endocrine gland function. He really knew his stuff and was fascinated with the subtopic of pigmentation science, which he had clearly mastered. Indeed, Mac was so enamored of the peptide α-MSH, he named his daughter Martha S. Hadley so she would have the initials "MSH."

The real "lightning strike" with the afamelanotide development story was the timing. In the mid-1980s, my friend and mentor, oncologist Dave Alberts, MD, had switched his very successful science program in cancer therapeutics to cancer prevention. Prevention was an entirely open canvas at that point in the early 1980s, and the National Cancer Institute (NCI) was literally hungry for projects to fund. At planning meetings with Mac, Victor, and Norm Levine, I proposed that we present the development of MT-I as a project in Dr. Alberts upcoming grant submission- a Program Project Grant (PPG) for Skin Cancer Prevention. There would be three to four projects in the PPG application, and one was proposed to be the preclinical and early clinical development of MT-I as a preventive agent for skin cancers, excluding melanomas. As stated earlier, this was truly a case of not knowing that we weren't really supposed to do such overarching drug development as mere academics. Those things were typically the province of large pharmaceutical companies with deep pockets and deep expertise in drug development. But sometimes, ignorance, and a little naïve bravado, can carry the day. We got the grant funded, and the entire team was ecstatic. We've already described the subsequent development effort, but there was another Hadley "incident" with this drug.

In the mid-1990s, Mac traveled to Japan for the yearly meeting of the International Pigmentation Society. It is a typical scientific conclave with platform presentations and poster sessions attended by many researchers from across the globe. Unbeknownst to us, at least to me, Mac had started to regularly inject himself with lower doses of MT-2, following the somewhat disastrous initial dosing "incident." We could all see that he was visibly darker and didn't think that much about it. But one day before leaving for the meeting, he had come out and said he was regularly injecting himself with MT-2, precisely as an "experiment" to be revealed at the meeting in Japan. Norm Levine immediately stated that he had wondered if Mac was doing that since his long-standing ruddy complexion due to rosacea had largely vanished.

So, Mac is at the meeting in Japan and talking with one of the premier pigmentation MD, PhD professors from a prestigious US East Coast university. Note this took place outside the main lecture hall during one of the coffee breaks in the large and bustling foyer to the lecture hall. After some initial pleasantries, the professor said: "Mac, have you been on a cruise? You're really tanned." It was exactly what Mac had been waiting for and he pounced: "No, I've been taking our cyclic α-MSH analog." The East Coast professor then chortled and said: "C'mon, Mac, you live in Tucson, Arizona. It's the sunlight capital." Mac was ready. He said: "If I showed you that my genitals were darker, would you then believe me?" Not believing anything would come of it, the person said, "Yeah, sure." Big mistake. Mac dropped his trousers right there in the coffee break area and revealed his very dark genitals to a horrified professor. (Note that the genitals in both sexes of humans have very high levels of melanocortin-1 receptors [MC1r], so they are especially sensitive to α-MSH and its derivatives). The astonished professor said: "Oh my God, Mac, I see, I see, please stop." Mac had proved his point and was not the least modest about it. Indeed, he proudly told us all about it when he got back from the meeting, similarly astounding us yet again. With anyone but Mac Hadley, we would not have believed it. And yet, Mac had replicated Francis Bacon's conundrum: why have an academic argument about how many teeth a horse has when you can just go and count the teeth?

On Thursday morning, November 16, 2006, I got a call from a reporter from the local paper, *The Arizona Daily Star*. He asked me if I had any comments on the death of UA Professor Emeritus, Mac E. Hadley. I was dumbstruck, as I was at a morning meeting with Mac the day before at the cancer center. We had adjourned at noon, with me wishing I'd ordered lunch for the group, as the meeting had gone into the lunch hour. I had no idea what had happened and said so. When that Wednesday meeting adjourned, Mac had bought some fast food and drove to his home on Tucson's west side. Later that afternoon, his body was discovered in the smoldering rear bedroom of his home. Several callers reported thick black smoke coming from the residence at about 3:30 P.M. The firefighters took about thirteen minutes to extinguish the flames and discovered the body. His wife, Gertrude (Trudy), had come home just after that with the firefighters still mopping up. Thankfully, she noticed that Mac's white Toyota was not there, so she initially assumed he was not home. But the firefighters and police told her that a body had indeed been found. While it had not yet been officially identified, they believed it was her husband's body. Poor Trudy—she had immediate chest pains and was rushed to the hospital intensive care unit, suffering a major heart attack.

It did not take the Tucson Police Department very long to find a suspect—someone was using Mac's cell phone in Nogales, AZ, on the US side of the international border with Mexico. They localized the cell signal to a small neighborhood and found Mac's white 1996 Toyota Camry parked outside a residence. With a search warrant, police entered and found Marco A. Chavez, thirty-one, who was living at his mother's house. Inside, they also found electronics and possessions worth four thousand dollars from the Hadley residence.

Marco Chavez had prior convictions for burglary, theft, and possession of stolen property. Only Chavez knows the precise details of what transpired, and he never gave up that information. The autopsy of Mac revealed a bullet jacket and fragments in his head. At the crime scene, police recovered bloody clothing, pieces of a baseball bat, fingerprints, and DNA that ultimately came back to Chavez. Chavez had apparently been part of a burglary ring that would drop off participants in different neighborhoods and then scoop up the person and the stolen goods a little later. Since the front door of Mac's house had been kicked in, we can assume that when Mac arrived home, he knew someone had broken in. Of course, the prudent thing at that point would have been to call the police, but that was not Mac Hadley. It was not the Mac Hadley with the Marines in Korea and not the somewhat pugnacious professor Mac Hadley. He was not going to let someone get away with robbing his home. So, we can guess that Mac picked up a baseball bat and went after Chavez, and there was a struggle. At some point, Mac was shot in the head, and the room was set on fire to try and destroy evidence.

But what kind of moron continues to use the decedent's cell phone and car, parking the latter outside where you are living? Needless to say, Chavez was readily convicted and sentenced to the maximum sentence on each of the five charges, all to run consecutively. That took the death penalty off the table but meant that Chavez will die in prison with the final sentence of life, plus eighty-eight years. Aggravating factors at the sentencing were Mac's age of seventy-six and Chavez's criminal history.

Mac Eugene Hadley was born on June 16, 1930, in San Jose, CA. He received his bachelor's degree from San Jose State College and his doctorate from Brown University in Providence, RI. He had very humble beginnings but became a world expert in pigmentation science. He was a professor of biology at the University of Arizona for forty years, and he changed the world. He made major discoveries in endocrinology and personally championed the development of the melanotropic peptide analogs of α-MSH. Mac Hadley was truly a force of nature. He served his country as a Navy hospital corpsman assigned to a US Marine Corps combat unit in Korea. He was an outstanding scientist and a true scholar. With every success of the melanotropic drugs, I actually ache that he and his family were robbed of the satisfaction and honor of his major accomplishments. But Mac does live on in those accomplishments.

# Chapter 13
## *Final Curtain*

*Terry explains his final exit and laments what might have been*

As 2007 began, we were still in shock over Mac's sudden death, but life had to go on. I was pressed for time because I had situations arise in two of our other start-ups out of UA and Arizona State U that required attention, and I was spending a lot of time in China where the clinical trial of "foie gras" was coming to a successful conclusion. I was grateful that Clinuvel was not taking much of my time. Philippe in Melbourne and Hank in Philadelphia were polishing the details of the work needed to start the clinical trials in EPP and PMLE. This included learning how to make a stable, reproducible form of the controlled release implant and making sure that our supplier of MT-1 was carrying out the manufacturing to the high standards of the FDA and analyzing the product with FDA-approved testing. This sounds straightforward, but Hank was an old warrior and kept reminding everyone that the most common reason for drugs to fail is defects with the product manufacturing and purity, known in the trade as CMC (chemistry, manufacturing, and controls). He was therefore paranoid about getting everything right.

Of all the CMC items, the one that gave us most trouble was the implant, and we developed a lot of know-how about manufacturing it to release the dose correctly. That achievement would be difficult for others to copy.

In February, Philippe asked me to accompany him to meet Florian in Mallorca and then go to see a company in France that was interested in discussing a potential corporate deal. I was not excited about having a large company involved, but I felt that we were now in a strong enough position that we could negotiate a very favorable deal. We started the trip in Geneva, seeing a couple of investors, then met with Florian in Mallorca and headed to France for the corporate meeting, which was a debacle. In spite of careful scheduling beforehand, the key executives we were to meet had been called out of town and did not bother to tell us, and so, we showed up to be informed that there was no meeting. There were a lot of comments about French business manners, but we simply returned to our respective domiciles. The one positive is that it cured some of us from being interested in big pharma partnering.

Both of the friction points between me and Philippe that I mentioned in chapter eleven started to worsen in this new year. The first was the composition of the board. We both wanted Wayne to step down since he did not add value at this stage, but we could not agree on whom to add. My strong feeling was that we needed to add several pharmaceutical industry executives who had developed a drug before and taken it to market. But Philippe was adamant that he wanted people from outside the industry arguing that would give us a much better perspective. He pushed for a lady who had been a successful stockbroker in Melbourne. She was a fine, smart person but had no experience of the drug industry. However, after speaking my piece, I backed off, and she joined the board in February. This seems to be the Australian way since you see it on the board of most companies. But that practice is not productive since boards should have a deep knowledge of the business in which the company operates in order to oversee the company's strategy. Most people in the US venture capital industry think the same way, and from the agonizingly long period of time it subsequently took to get MT-1 to market, we may be correct. No board comprised of industry executives would have tolerated these delays.

The second friction point was the company's strategic focus. I continued to argue to prioritize a focus on the cosmetic tanning market, especially now that we had raised enough capital, and could raise much more, to do this. Philippe was strongly against it and favored the Botox strategy of a highly targeted initial indication that was discussed in chapter four. With that strategy, we would get an initial approval in a rare orphan disease such as EPP and then add indications from there with possible off-label use as a bonus, as with Botox. My response was that this strategy would take too long, and by the time we got to the cosmetic market, our patents would have expired. And further, the FDA would not allow generous off label use as they did with Botox. I think that subsequent events have validated this position.

At the end of March 2007, we decided that we should raise the full complement of funding to go through market launch, and Florian arranged a European roadshow with investor presentations in Vienna, Paris, London, and Zürich. We decided to have the same format as the prior presentations, with Florian introducing us, me giving the main presentation, and Philippe speaking last to highlight the risks. The presentations were timed for late afternoon with an investor dinner afterwards. I was amazed at the large number of investors who attended all of these meetings.

The Vienna meeting was particularly well attended, and in the cocktail hour preceding the presentations, I learned that Vienna has been the center of dermatology in Europe since the early 1900s. I heard stories of eminent Austrian dermatologists, of the drugs and procedures they had developed and the well-heeled patients who had flocked to Vienna to be treated for their skin ailments. The specialty of these Viennese dermatologists had been, and still is, the cosmetic problems of their clientele, and so, they were uniquely qualified to pass judgment on Clinuvel's product and the science underlying it. This accounted for the good attendance and for the keen interest and spirited questions and discussion following our presentations. In fact, the Q&A session was the liveliest one we had yet had and included some challenging questions on safety that Philippe handled well.

After the Q&A session ended, we proceeded to dinner in an adjacent room where my wife and I were seated at a large circular table with about twelve people. Everyone spoke impeccable English, and the conversation began almost before I was seated. It went something like this:

The well-dressed young gentleman to my left said, "Well, Terry, that was a very interesting presentation, but I am very disappointed that you did not address the only reason why I already invested in this company, and that is your plans for the cosmetic tanning market. That is the major upside for this company and not these small orphan markets. You did not even mention the cosmetic uses, and that is the main interest of most of the investors at this presentation." There were murmurs of agreement around the table as I stole a quick glance at the nodding heads.

I must confess that I was totally taken off guard, and it took all of my media training not to show it. I took some deep breaths, looked around the table, and slowly responded, "I appreciate your question, but I'm not sure where you got the impression that we plan to focus on the cosmetic tanning market since we have never included that in our presentation or any of our fundraising materials." I was secretly wishing that I could tell them of my true feelings and my efforts to do exactly what they were advocating.

The young gentleman quickly responded, "Well, yes, you are correct, but we thought that everybody knew that the cosmetic market is your true target, just like Botox." I really did not want to get into a discussion about Botox because that would lead to the inevitable subject of off-label promotion, which was a hot topic at this time with FDA. There was at least one ongoing lawsuit where FDA was suing a US company for off-label promotion, whose defense was that this is simply an expression of their constitutionally guaranteed free-speech. This could have been a difficult subject to discuss at dinner. So, I tried to steer the conversation around to discuss all of the other potential indications for a tanning drug and also inject some humor by talking about the related sexual stimulation drug. We then had a very entertaining dinner conversation about a wide range of subjects.

But, as dinner was breaking up, an older gentleman at the table reminded me of the opportunity in cosmetic tanning and asked if I would review the situation with Clinuvel management since this would be crucial to whether they would invest in the company. I agreed to do so.

It was now late, and everyone was tired, especially me, since I had flown in from the USA that day and was by now exhausted. So, I did not have a chance to review this with Philippe until the next day, a Sunday, in Paris, which we had set aside to review the presentations, ready for the Paris meeting on Monday. In our review session in a hotel near the Madeleine, I related the discussion at dinner in Vienna to Philippe, and I suggested that we include some reference to it in our presentations. But, in spite of a sometimes-heated discussion, he would have none of it and insisted on the orphan drug strategy. I was not happy. The presentations the next day at the Hotel de Crillon on Place de la Concorde went well. The audience was not as large as in Vienna, and the Q&A was more subdued. Then we took the Chunnel train to London.

The London meeting promised to be at least as well attended as Vienna but with more high net-worth people, and so, it was the pivotal meeting of this fund-raising road show. Before the meeting, we had another session to review the presentations, and I again raised the cosmetic tanning issue but, this time, in a different way. Rather than asking for the whole thing, I tried to get a small concession and said that we could increase our impact if I started off my main presentation with a photo of the before and after tanning effect on one of the Arizona student volunteers—we had several such photos. After the usual spirited discussion, it was agreed that we would do so, and I incorporated this as my first slide after the introduction.

The London meeting was in the Dorchester Hotel on Park Lane. We were in the large meeting room on the top floor for the presentation after lunch, and there were a lot people there. Florian gave an outstanding introduction and talked about the fact that in his long career, he had seen only a small handful of opportunities that were unique and had a very large upside—Clinuvel is one of those such opportunities. I was up next and moved straight to the before-and-after slide of the Arizona student's face, emphasizing that the difference was caused by the drug and that sunlight was carefully eliminated. You could feel the buzz in the room as the slide was shown and explained. The rest of the presentation went well, and I carefully avoided mentioning the cosmetic tanning market. Philippe then talked about the risks, and there was a good but uneventful Q&A.

That evening, we had a dinner with Florian and some of the London-based investors and wives at the very top of the Dorchester around a circular table that seated about twenty in a private room. The view over the London landscape was outstanding, the people were fascinating, and the conversation was most enjoyable. Then we moved on to Zürich for the final presentation, which continued to include the before-and-after photo. My wife and I then flew directly to Beijing and on to Luoyang in China where my VTL company was to present the successful results of our China trial and to plan the writing of the formal application to apply to the Chinese FDA for approval to market our liver failure product in China.

About a week later, I learned that the EU roadshow had raised over A$60 million and that the company was now extremely well financed through the expected product launch. Soon after, the money was in the bank.

Clinuvel had already opened satellite offices in Zurich and in San Francisco, and our April board meeting was held at the San Francisco office. It was after this board meeting that I decided to resign from the board. The main reason was that I continued to find myself in disagreement with Philippe on numerous issues, and it was obvious that the board was supporting him on all of them. It is no fun being the lone voice of dissent on a board, and I was not going to compromise my integrity by simply going along with the flow, like happens on many boards. I did not need the income, and it looked to me that the company was now well established. It should be successful no matter how it was managed. The only question was the degree of that success. And it was obvious to me that my dream of building a large company that would dominate its markets was impossible with the current team. Further, I was now the CEO of "foie-gras" and one other company. Thus, my time was over committed, and I was better off without the ongoing distraction of Clinuvel.

I have shared two of the key issues of disagreement, board composition and strategic focus, but I don't think it is appropriate to discuss the others. Suffice to say that they were substantial, and there were some difficult board discussions. But I was a minority of one on a board that I did not respect and one that did not respect me. I was probably right on some points and wrong on others. Therefore, it was best for all parties that I quietly stepped down. It had been a lot of fun, and I lament what could have been. As Florian said in his introductions to our fundraising presentations, these kinds of opportunities are few and far between, and I regret that I did not do a better job and get it on the road to becoming a very large company.

What makes an opportunity like this in the life sciences? After a career spent in looking for them and analyzing the results of the twenty-one such university-sourced start-ups that we did, I believe that there are three main boxes that have to be checked:

1. Addressing a very large market, at least US$1 billion/year worldwide
2. Strong competitive position, preferably with no direct competitors, and a wide moat around the potential business (shades of Buffett's criteria)
3. Strong intellectual property protection. This is usually through patents, but there are other forms of IP including know-how, government exclusivities, and unique teams

Melanotan/Epitan/Clinuvel checked these three boxes with room to spare. These same criteria could be used to quickly reject 90 percent of the start-up business plans we received at our VC fund. You will note that the three boxes do not include anything about the people factor. While people can destroy a great opportunity, they cannot make a success out of an unattractive opportunity. I would sooner invest in an "A" business with "B" people than the reverse. As the renowned Omaha investor Warren Buffett says: you want to invest in a great business that a lousy management cannot screw up.

After I resigned, I did not have a window on the inside of the company, and I lost contact with all the board members. However, in spite of being well capitalized, it took them eight more years to get the drug approved in the EU and four additional years to get FDA approval in the USA. It should have taken less than half that time. And when it did finally get EU approval for EPP, it came with draconian terms that allowed it to be prescribed only by physicians who treated EPP. So, we were correct that the regulators were not going to allow another Botox situation where the product grew by off-label use. And these approvals were only for EPP, a tiny market of less than five thousand patients worldwide. And all the time, the patent clock was ticking down the time to expiration in about 2025, and the threat of generic competitors after the orphan exclusivity expires in 2026, which will probably happen.

These comments are not meant to belittle the achievement of gaining approval for the product in the EU and USA. Any such approval is the result of a lot of hard work and commitment, and I salute the management team for this accomplishment. I believe this is the first drug that has been developed and marketed internationally by an Australian company without the involvement of a large pharmaceutical company partner. I am sure that they will build a nice, profitable, small biopharmaceutical company.

Current revenues (4Q20) are running at an annual rate of A$21M (US$16M). With better management and a more aggressive strategy, the company could have achieved so much more, especially if the main focus had been on the cosmetic tanning opportunity. You need only look to the value of the Botox franchise (this is difficult since it is buried in a large company) to see that the market cap could now have been more than ten times higher. I am sure that the product will eventually be used for cosmetic tanning purposes and for such other large markets as skin cancer prevention. But there will probably be weak intellectual property protection and several competitors at that future time which will make for a generic pharmaceutical product where the pricing will be relatively low and the margins weak. I hope the management team proves me wrong.

When the product was approved in the USA, the company was not ready to start full-fledged marketing in the USA and said that it would take about a year to initiate US revenues. They have actually done better than that, but pharmaceutical companies typically are ready to begin the product launch on the day of the drug's approval since they know the value of the limited-time patent and/or orphan drug monopoly. This was not only a disappointment to all the US EPP patients, but it has wasted patent/orphan drug exclusivity time. The company still has only modest revenues with the two EU and US approvals and no second product near the market. A board with more pharma experience would never have allowed the US unpreparedness to happen and would have been much further along with new indications for approval.

When I think of the benefits that could have been generated from a cosmetic tanning approval and the number of skin cancers that would probably have been prevented by the elimination of the UV light from the tanning salons, I am sad! But at least the product is on the market, all be it for a micro market opportunity. Ah, well, you can't win them all!

We hope you have enjoyed this story. Now, immerse yourself in the science of tanning in Part Two.

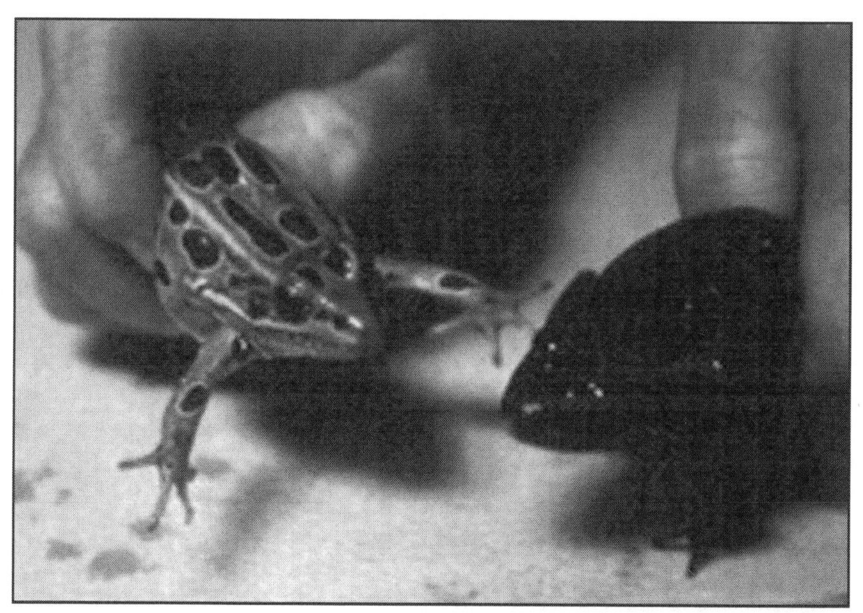

Two *rana Pipiens*, Northern Tree frogs, untreated on the left and treated with afamelanotide on the right. The treated frogs never revert to normal pigmentation due to the superpotency of afamelanotide. Professor Hadley used the frog skin bioassay to survey hundreds of potential melanotropins before afamelanotide (originally Melanotan-1) was selected for human clinical development.

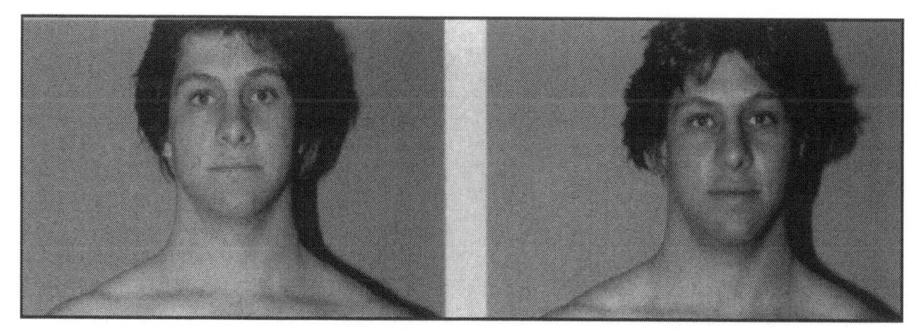

Normal volunteer before (left) and after (right) treatment with afamelanotide for two weeks in the phase I/II clinical trial performed at the University of Arizona. Reprinted with permission from the Journal of the American Medical Association, Volume 266, Nov, 20, 1991.

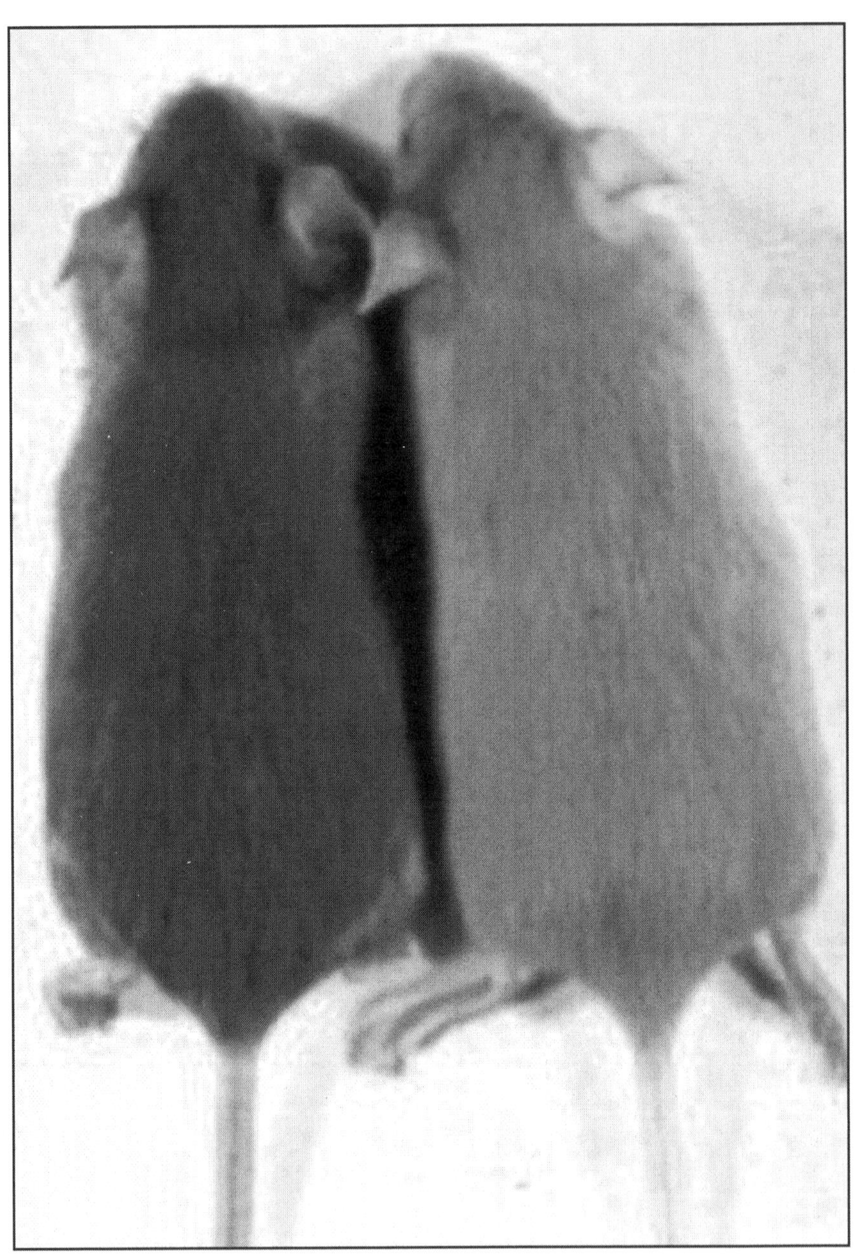

Two mice, originally with red hair, one treated with afamelanotide (left, brown hair), and one untreated (right, red hair). This showed that the drug could change the type of melanin from pheomelanin (red) to eumelanin (brown).

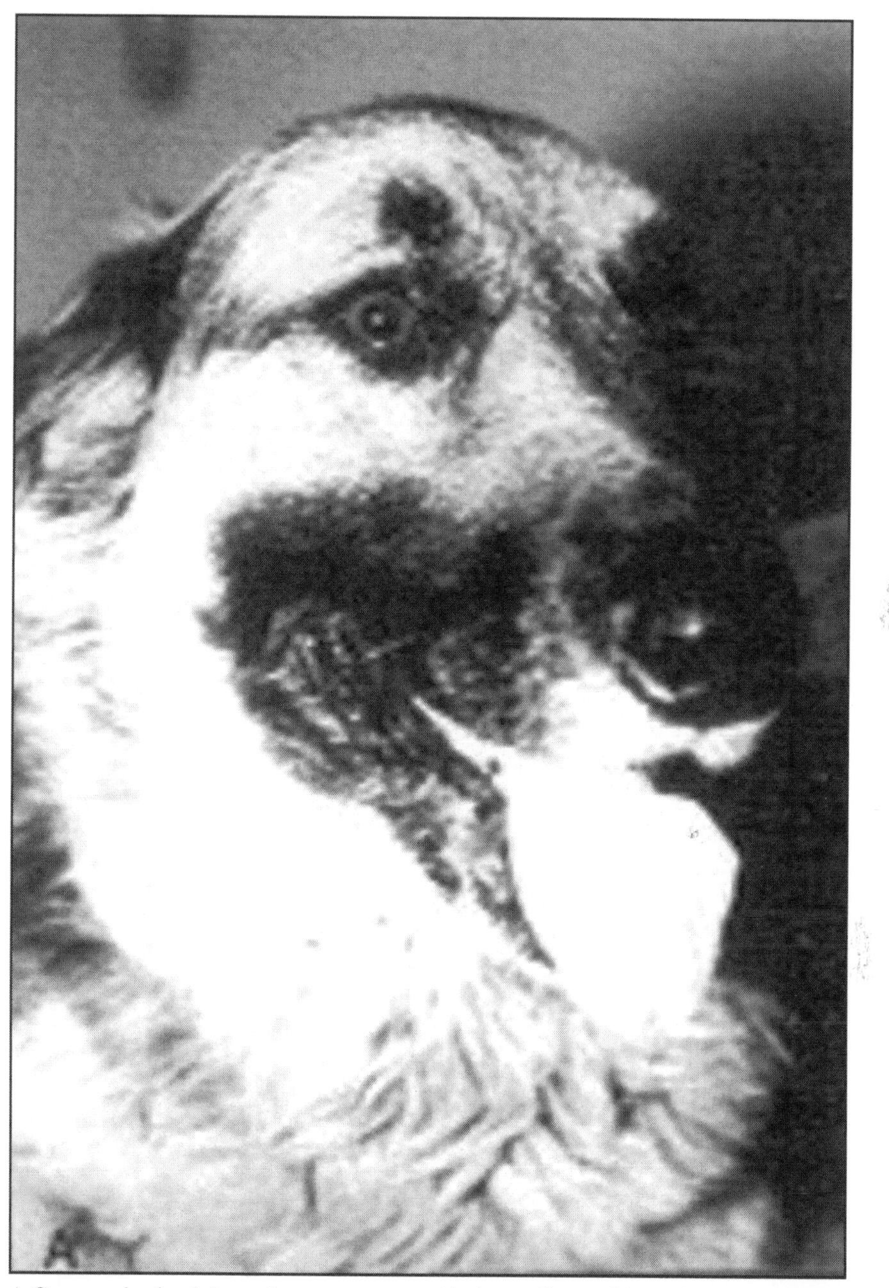

A German shepherd dog prior to treatment with the cyclic peptide Melanotan-2 (MT-2). Reprinted with permission from the American Journal of Veterinary Research, Volume 55, November, 1994.

The same dog after 2 weeks of treatment with MT-2. Reprinted from the same Am J Vet Res Vol 55, November 1994.

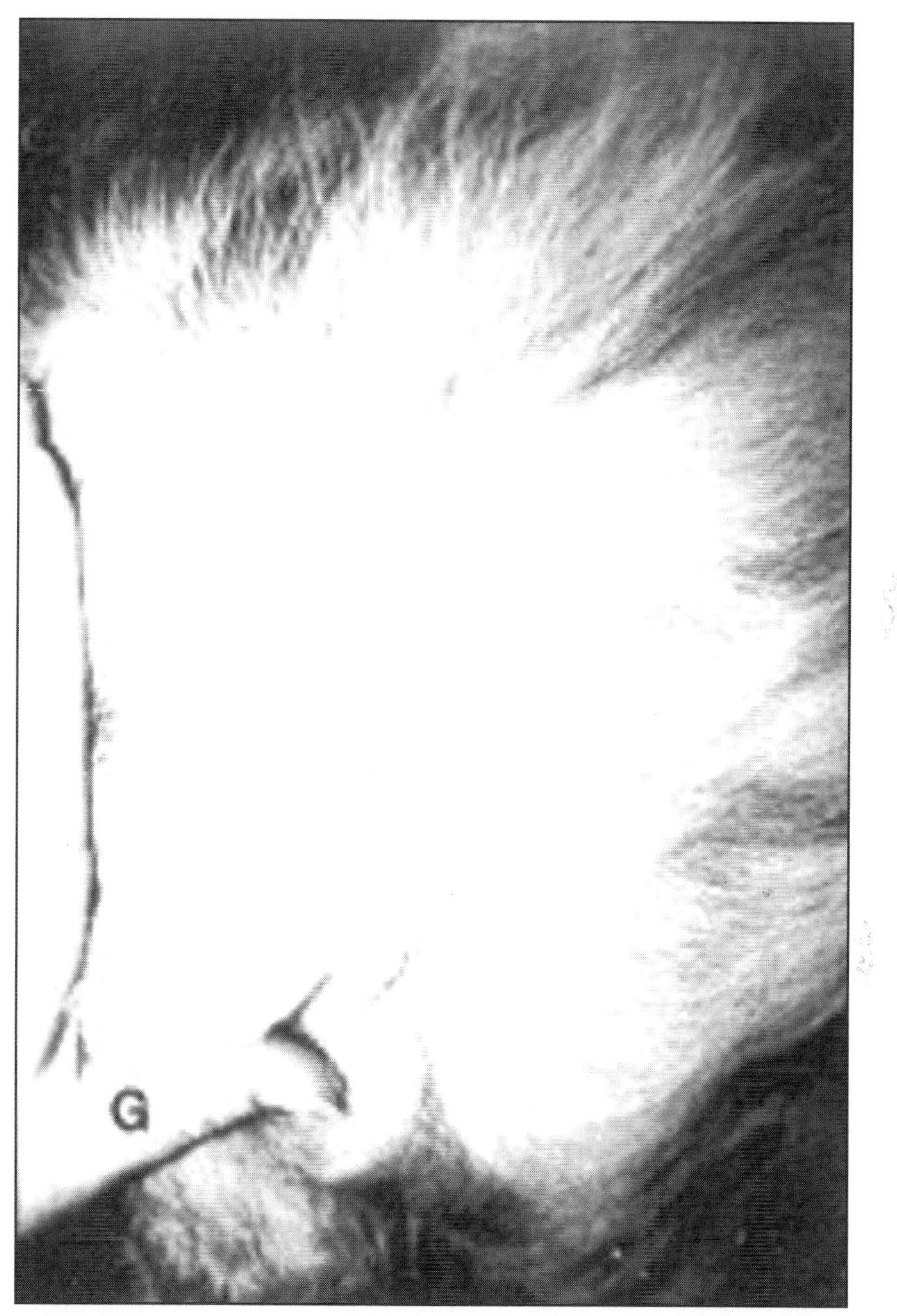


A closeup photo of the same dog's normal coat color prior to dosing with MT-2. Reprinted with permission from the Amer J Vet Res, Vol. 55, 1994.

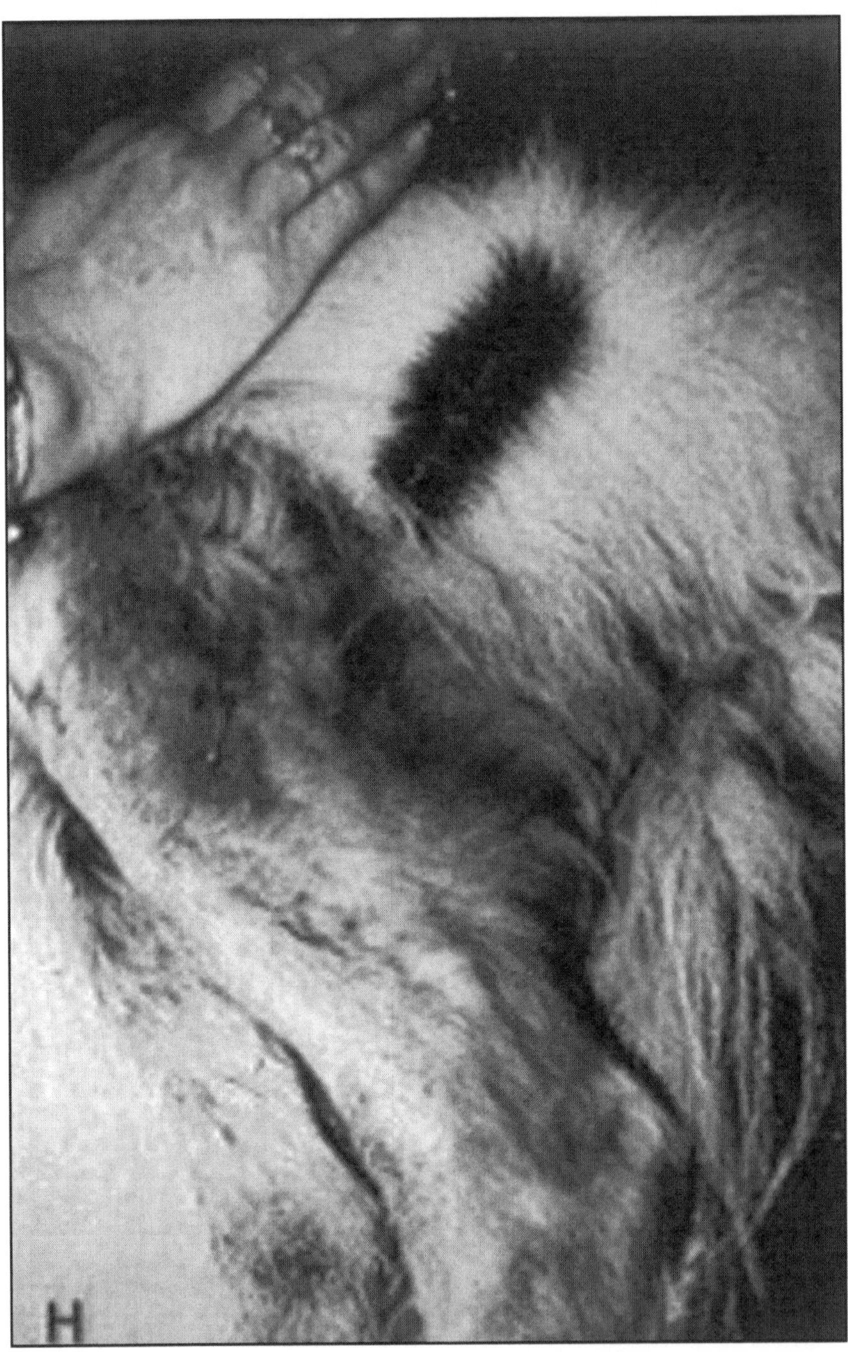


A closeup photo of the same dog's coat color, showing the band of pigmentation following treatment with MT-2. Reprinted with permission from the Amer J Vet Res, Vol. 55, November 1994.

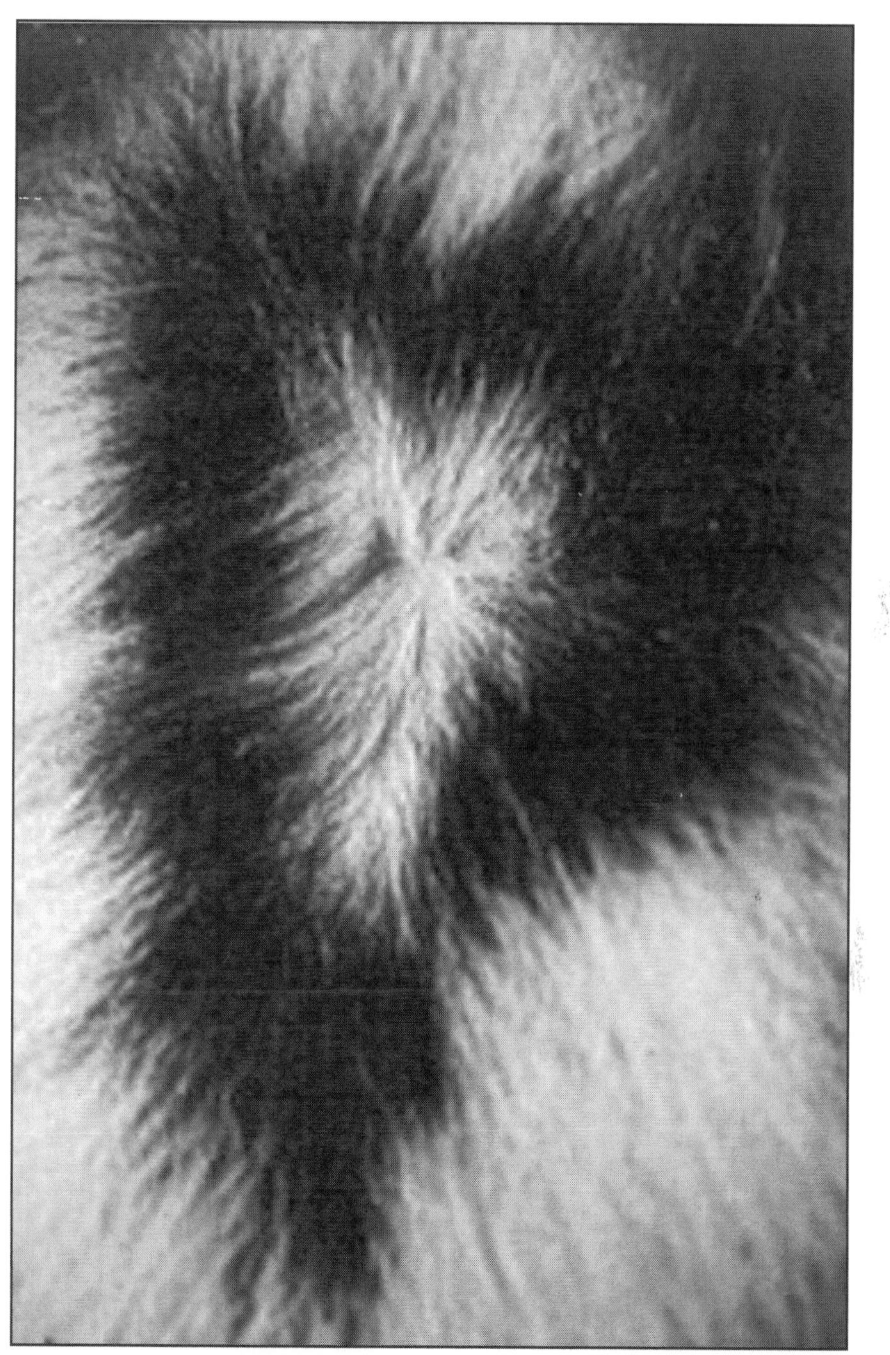

A closeup of the further band of pigmentation in the same dog's coat color, 4 weeks after dosing. Reprinted with permission from the Amer J Vet Res, Vol. 55, November 1994.

The melanotropin development team at the University of Arizona in circa, 1990. From left to right: biologist Mac Hadley, Ph.D., pharmacologist Robert Dorr, Ph.D., dermatologist Norman Levine, MD, and senior chemist, Professor Victor Hruby, Ph.D.

The University of Arizona peptide chemistry team, circa 1983. From left to right: Chris Heward, Ph.D., biologist, Professor Mac Hadley, PhD., senior laboratory chemist, Professor Victor Hruby, Ph.D., afamelanotide synthesizer, (then graduate student), Tomi Sawyer, Ph.D.

# PART 2
# The Science of Tanning

### All you ever wanted to know about tanning, the details of the clinical development work at the University of Arizona and the story of MT-2

This part was written by Bob and goes into the science and technical detail. We suggest that you try to read it since we think you will find it fascinating, and you can skip some of the more technical parts.

# Chapter 14

## *How Do We Tan: The Science of Human Pigmentation*

Humans are an oddity in the animal kingdom in terms of pigmentation, which, for early hominids, started as an evolutionary adaptation to the loss of body hair about 1.2 million years go. Humans don't change color with the seasons as some animals like the snow hare do. We also lack a thick coat of body hair like the rest of the primates have retained to prevent sun damage of the underlying skin. In that regard, we are clearly the so-called "naked apes" of evolutionary lore and ridicule. But we do come in a variety of skin tones, from deep black to pale white and every variation in between. How can that be? Well, the answer lies in our location-mediated evolutionary paths to adapt to varying amounts of sunlight: dark skin in the sun-drenched tropical latitudes and light skin in the sparse sunlight of northern latitudes. And, in terms of human existence, these are clearly relatively recent evolutionary adaptions from a uniformly dark-colored common African ancestry of only a few hundred thousand years ago.

If we look at mammals that change coat color with the seasons, we find that they rely on a part of the pituitary gland in the brain not found in humans, the pars intermedia, which is located in the anterior lobe (front) part of the pituitary. In mammals with the pars intermedia, light input to the retina activates the release of the pigmentary hormone, melanocyte stimulating hormone, or MSH, into the bloodstream. We'll have much more on that molecule later. For example, the snow hare releases MSH from the pars intermedia, which circulates in the bloodstream. This gradually turns the coat color from pale white in the winter to dark brown in the summer. That seasonal adaption to ambient sunlight allows for coat color camouflage in both the winter (no MSH = white coat color) and the summer

(MSH=brown coat color). The same eye-brain-body color axis also works in lizards and frogs, only the changes can be nearly instantaneous as the brain is directly wired to their equivalent of our melanocytes in mammals, and the melanophores in reptiles and amphibians. But humans lack the pars intermedia that is responsible for central (brain) signaling of MSH as in the snow hare. We also lack the hard wiring for the brain to directly connect to the melanocytes in the body as with a chameleon that has melanophores. So, again, how do we change our pigmentation, or tan, if you will?

## Understanding Ultraviolet (UV) Radiation from the Sun

In the electromagnetic spectrum, UV light from the sun comes in three forms: UVA, UVB, and UVC. We won't discuss UVC since it is completely absorbed by the ozone layer and the atmosphere. But that is not so for UVA, which has wavelengths of 315–399 nm and is not absorbed by the ozone layer. UVA is present every day. It can pass through glass and is unaffected by altitude or weather. It is twenty times more abundant than UVB and is the most common form of UV light at the Earth's surface. While UVA is weaker than UVB in terms of energy, it penetrates deeper into the skin and can damage the underlying dermis layer. However, UVA is viewed as less cancer-causing (carcinogenic) than UVB. Most tanning beds use UVA light sources because of the supposed lower cancer risk, but a UVA-induced "tan" is far less protective against sun damage to the epidermis, which contains the keratinocyte and melanocyte cells that *do* pose a cancer risk. UVA-induced tans also thicken and prematurely age the skin over time, indicating a different type of long-term damage.

So that leaves UVB as the major light energy "player" in human pigmentation (and skin cancer). UVB is defined as wavelengths of light 280–314 nm and is incompletely absorbed by the ozone layer. But enough does reach the Earth's surface to cause both tanning and, with excess exposure over time, skin cancer. UVB cannot pass through glass but has higher energy than UVA and penetrates to the epidermis, where both tanning and skin cancers arise. UVB light energy is strongest in the middle of the day in the summer and intensifies as one nears the equator. There are some beneficial effects of UVB, such as aiding in Vitamin D synthesis, which is important for developing and maintaining bone density. But by far, UVB has a more malign potential to induce cancers of the skin and eye as well as cataracts. This is because the shorter wavelengths of light in the UVB range are precisely those wavelengths around 280 nm that are associated with cellular DNA damage. The two main types of DNA damage from UVB are DNA strand breaks and DNA intra-strand dimer formation, which we'll explain a bit later.

There are three types of skin cancers associated with UVB: basal cell carcinoma, the more-deadly squamous cell carcinoma, and the often-fatal, malignant melanomas. Cumulative UVB exposure over one's lifetime is highly correlated with the non-melanoma skin cancers, basal cell and squamous cell cancers. This is especially true for fair-skinned, poorly tanning individuals, and the risk increases significantly for those with red hair. The correlation with lifetime UVB exposure is less strong for melanomas, but UVB is still a known contributor. So, human pigmentation has largely been, and remains, an adaptive evolutionary change to control DNA damage from the UVB band of energy in sunlight.

This leads us to the numerical classification scheme for response to UVB in humans—the Fitzpatrick scale. The scale was published by Thomas Fitzpatrick in 1975 as a means of categorizing an individual's response to sunlight into six numerical types (Table 1). The scale has proven useful as a tool to predict those individuals who may need greater sun protection and ranges from white, non-pigmented individuals, Types I and II, to those pigmented people who can tolerate sun exposure with minimal negative effects, Types V and VI. Type VI individuals are almost always black-skinned.

We used the Fitzpatrick scale to select patients for the initial clinical trials of afamelanotide, then called Melanotan-I, since we wanted to exclude those that do not tan and burn easily in sunlight (Types I and II), and those that are already highly-pigmented (Types V and VI). So, we chose the most common Caucasian skin types of III and IV for the afamelanotide trial, who have some pigment and tan easily. It was a good decision, because we were able to see significant increased pigmentation without any serious skin toxicity.

## Table 1: The Fitzpatrick Skin Type Scale

| Skin | Type of Sun Exposure Reaction History (physical appearance) |
|---|---|
| I | Always burns, never tans (palest, freckles) |
| II | Usually burns, tans minimally |
| III | Sometimes mild burn, tans uniformly |
| IV | Burns minimally, always tans well (moderate brown) |
| V | Very rarely burns (deeply pigmented dark brown to darkest brown) |
| VI | Never burns (deeply pigmented dark brown to darkest brown) |

Fitzpatrick TB (1975) Journal de Medecine Esthetique (2): 33-34.

## Sun Damage and α-MSH

It turns out that humans have preserved the ability to respond to MSH stimulation of skin pigmentation, but the source of that MSH is not the pituitary gland in the brain. Rather, humans rely on the release of MSH from skin cells called keratinocytes, or we'll just shorten that to "K-cells." Those K-cells primarily reside in the outer layers of the skin, i.e., the epidermal layer that will be the first to be exposed to ultraviolet (UV) light from the sun. K-cells constitute 90 percent of the cells in the epidermis, which provides the main skin barrier against infectious agents, UV-damage, and water loss. When present in the basal layer of the skin, K-cells are referred to as basal cells. Sun-damaged K-cells exhibit a specific type of acute response that, if severe, causes the K-cells to die by a normal process called apoptosis, or "programmed cell death." However, chronic, non-lethal sun damage causes changes in the keratinocytes leading to rough, scaly clusters of damaged K-cells called actinic keratoses, or AKs, which are pre-cancerous skin lesions. AKs are routinely removed by dermatologists using liquid nitrogen. If the AKs are extensive and recurring, they can be treated with several weeks of daily 5-fluorouracil (5-FU) cream applied directly to the affected areas of the skin, known as topical application. Note that 5-FU is a well-known anticancer agent that is routinely given by the IV route, directly into the patient's bloodstream, for many types of solid tumors. It is an old but good chemotherapy drug and acts by killing cells that are undergoing cell division. Since cancer cells, including AKs, are more rapidly dividing, 5-FU preferentially kills them along with other rapidly dividing cells. This clearly demonstrates the link between chronic sun damage by UV-light to the K-cells and the development of cancer.

We "tan" following sunlight exposure based on the degree of DNA damage to the K-cells. That's right, every tan is induced by DNA damage to your K-cells. The damage to the K-cells' DNA elicits those cells to release MSH as a signal for the melanocytes (M-cells) to start making melanin. The severity of K-cell DNA damage is directly correlated to how much MSH they release, and how much melanin is produced in the M-cells. But how do we know this? Skin biopsies performed before and after controlled UV exposures in volunteer subjects have documented a special kind of DNA damage in the K-cells—the formation of linked pairs of DNA pyrimidine bases, the so-called pyrimidine dimers. The bases become chemically linked by the light energy from the UV exposure. These dimers, or pairs of the pyrimidine bases thymine and cytosine, occur in a single strand of DNA. The result is the formation of an intra-strand (same strand), crosslink, called a cyclobutane dimer, or CBD (not to be confused with cannabidiol). The CBD from UV light damage is actually a four-membered chemical ring in a single strand of DNA. And the bonds formed in these DNA bases are covalent, the strongest type of chemical linkage known. Thus, they constitute a direct mutation in that DNA strand. These CBD mutations can also lead to cancer formation (carcinogenesis) if they cannot be repaired by the damaged cells. And that includes both K-cells and M-cells. We'll have more on DNA repair later, but many studies have clearly shown that the number of CBD dimers formed is proportional to the amount of UV light exposure *and* inversely proportional to the degree of pigmentation present at the time of exposure. As you would expect, the darker the skin at the time of exposure, the fewer CBD dimers that are formed, indicating less DNA damage, for given amount of UV. That is exactly why black skin is so amazingly protective against DNA damage to the skin, and dramatically reduces the incidence of skin cancer in darker-skinned individuals. So, black really IS beautiful in terms of skin protection from the damaging effects of sunlight. And, by the way, blacks don't have *more* M-cells in their skin. They have *more active* M-cells in their skin, M-cells that do not rely on sun exposure to maintain the protective dark skin color. And the first modern humans also had more active M-cells than current Caucasians. So, the loss of color in Caucasians is a relatively late evolutionary adaptation to life in low sunlight environments.

Okay, so, we now understand that sunlight causes DNA damage in the K-cells, which induces the K-cells to release MSH into those sun-exposed skin areas. That MSH subsequently causes a "tan" (pigmentation) sometime afterwards, but how? It turns out that the MSH released by the K-cells following DNA damage is taken up by the nearby M-cells. M-cells are derived from nerve tissue and are basically modified neurons that don't carry an electrical message like brain neurons, but rather, they relay a chemical (hormonal) message from the K-cells. In response to the release of MSH from the K-cells, the MSH molecule, the M-cells start to make the pigment melanin. When the melanin has been synthesized, it is put into small "packets" called melanosomes. It is then transported inside the M-cells to the outer "tentacles" of the octopus-shaped M-cells. Those melanin-rich melanosomes are then released from the M-cells to be taken up by the K-cells, thereby completing a hormonal signaling circuit. This completes the chemical message cycle that started with DNA damage in the K-cells.

That final "message" is the pigment melanin that the K-cells take up to protect their nuclei from further DNA damage from sunlight. Importantly, administering α-MSH, or a derivative like afamelanotide (Melanotan-1, Scenesse), bypasses the need for DNA damage to start the pigmentation cycle that leads to skin darkening (and skin cancers) (Figure 1). In that regard, the near thousand-fold increase in potency over natural α-MSH explains why afamelanotide is such an effective tanning agent.

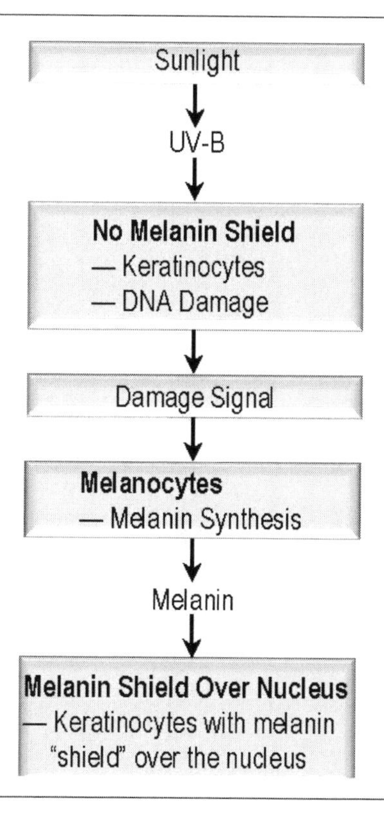


Figure 1: The "tanning" circuit in human skin showing that MSH carries the message of K-cell DNA damage to nearby M-cells. At the M-cells, MSH stimulates the production of melanin. Melanin is packaged into melanosomes and released back to the K-cells. This provides protection from further sunlight damage. In contrast, the injection of afamelanotide directly stimulates the M-cells, thereby obviating the need for DNA damage to initiate pigmentation (tanning).

The K-cells break down the melanosomes, releasing the melanin pigment intracellularly (inside) the K-cells. However, the K-cells do not distribute the melanin evenly across their cell's area. Rather, the melanin is positioned directly over the nucleus of the K-cells in line with the angle of light the cell is receiving. In other words, the K-cells use the melanin to form a "nuclear shield" to protect the K-cells' DNA from further sunlight damage. Now that is a neat trick. The only problem is, we had to get DNA damage to start the melanin pigmentation cycle going, and that unfortunate feature appears to be unique to humans.

## The Melanotropic Peptides

Now that we have the basics down for human pigmentation, we can delve a little deeper into all those molecular "players" in that process, starting with MSH. MSH is a peptide hormone. That means it is made up of amino acids bound in a string-like configuration using peptide bonds between each amino acid in the string. This gives rise to the chemical nomenclature that it is a "peptide" molecule. For reference, the best-known peptide hormone is probably insulin, which mediates diverse metabolic cellular functions, most notably glucose regulation. MSH is similarly a peptide hormone because it is composed of amino acids and can mediate a variety of effects, and not just pigmentation.

The MSH "family" of peptide hormones includes three closely related members: alpha-MSH (α-MSH), the primary pigmentation peptide hormone, beta-MSH (β-MSH), and gamma-MSH (ɣ-MSH). Because each of these peptides can induce pigmentation, they are collectively labelled the melanotropins and also the "melanocortins" if adrenocorticotrophic hormone (ACTH) is included. All of these peptides, including ACTH, are derived from a common large precursor peptide molecule called propiomelanocortin, or POMC. This POMC "master peptide" is produced in the pituitary and is then "clipped" or cleaved enzymatically into the various smaller peptides like a-MSH, ACTH, and the pain-reducing peptide precursors, beta-lipotropin (Figure 2). The gene responsible for producing the POMC peptide is also called POMC and is vital for the regulation of many functions other than pigmentation, including feeding and sexual behaviors. More on that later.

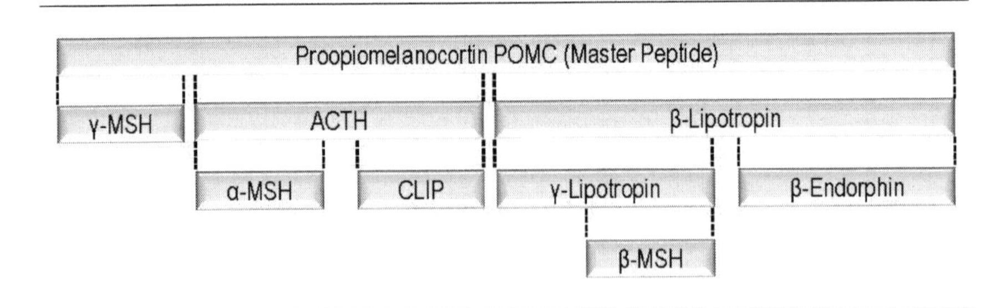


Figure 2: The precursor peptide POMC is initially cleaved to yield three peptides : ɣ-MSH, ACTH and β-lipotropin. ACTH is subsequently cleaved to yield α-MSH and CLIP, a peptide with unknown activity in humans. Beta lipotropin, which does not induce pigmentation, is cleaved into gamma (ɣ-) and beta β-) fragments that are eventually metabolized to the brain's primary pain killing peptide, beta endorphin.

We need to take a slight diversion to discuss ACTH briefly. ACTH is not a pigmentation molecule per se. It is secreted from the pituitary into the bloodstream to induce cortisol production in the adrenal glands of the kidney in response to daily needs of "stress management." There is a normal pre-dawn ACTH release which aids the body in awakening and managing routine daily stresses. However, severe stress can cause an abnormal release of ACTH to raise cortisol levels. In the short term, that can modulate stress, but chronic ACTH-cortisol levels weakens the body. Especially the immune system. This diversion about ACTH helps to explain certain human hyperpigmentation conditions since a-MSH is contained in the first thirteen amino acids in the thirty-nine-amino acid ACTH molecule. Thus, ACTH is the immediate precursor peptide which is cleaved to form α-MSH. Excess ACTH can also cause hyperpigmentation because it contains the α-MSH sequence. For example, the heightened ACTH levels in patients with Addison's Disease, also called primary adrenal insufficiency, can also cause hyperpigmentation of the skin. This was a well-observed state in perhaps the most famous Addison's Disease patient, President John F. Kennedy, who always appeared "tanned" like the actor George Hamilton. But ACTH itself has its own receptor in the adrenal glands, the melanocortin receptor-2 (MC2r), and therefore, ACTH is not regarded as a direct-acting melanotropic peptide.

The three true melanotropic peptides, alpha, beta, and gamma-MSH, have closely related amino acid structures and pigmentary properties. β-MSH and γ-MSH are minor players in human pigmentation, and their other biologic activities are not well understood. So, we will only focus on α-MSH, which is the primary pigmentation molecule and was the basis for the development of afamelanotide. The structure of natural or "native" α-MSH is linear, with thirteen amino acids in a precise sequence (Figure 3):

## The structures of MT-1 and MT-2 are compared to the natural hormone, alpha-MSH

α-MSH: Ac-Ser-Tyr-Ser-Met$_4$-Glu-His-Phe$_7$-Arg-Trp-Gly-Lys-Pro-Val$_{13}$-NH$_2$

MT-1: Ac-Ser-Tyr-Ser-**Nle$_4$**-Glu-His-D-**Phe$_7$**-Arg-Trp-Gly-Lys-Pro-Val$_{13}$-NH$_2$

MT-2: Ac-**Nle$_4$**-Asp-His-D-**Phe$_7$**-Arg-Trp-Gly-Lys--NH$_2$

Figure 3: The linear thirteen-amino acid (abbreviations) sequence of α-MSH which is acetylated at the N (nitrogen)-terminus and amidated at the C (carboxyl)-terminus. In comparison, the lower structure shows, in bold, the two amino acid substitutions (changes) that yield afamelanotide: a Norleucine (Nle) for methione (Met) at position 4 and a D-phenylalanine (Phe) for L-Phe at position 7.

## Melanocortin Receptors (MCr)

Now we know that α-MSH is the primary pigmentation peptide in humans and is released from sun-damaged K-cells to stimulate melanin production and dispersion by M-cells. But exactly how does that work? All the melanotropic peptides interact with target cells that express specific melanocortin receptors (MCr) for those peptides on their cell surface. This feature makes the melanotropic peptides very specific in their stimulatory activities because they will only affect cells that have those specific MCr receptors on their cell surface. That differs greatly from most small molecule (non-peptide) drugs which can and do penetrate into almost every cell in the body. This total-body exposure with most small-molecule drugs occurs even though the effects might only be needed in a specific organ, like the lungs for asthma patients or the heart and kidneys for blood pressure patients. So, receptor-specific drugs like MSH and afamelanotide add a real safety element and much more precise cellular targeting compared to small molecule-based non-specific drugs.

There are five subtypes of MCr which produce further specificity of stimulatory actions. Alpha-MSH induces pigmentation by binding to MCr1 receptors in M-cells in the skin. The MCr1 receptor internalizes the α-MSH molecule and causes a cascade of stimulatory activities inside the cells that result in melanin synthesis and release. ACTH has its own receptor, MCr2, which is not targeted by α-MSH nor the other two melanotropins (β-MSH and ɣ-MSH). The MCr3, MCr4, and MCr5 receptors are broadly distributed throughout the body but only minutely in the skin. For the skin, MCr1 is the "big kahuna" for pigmentation. In contrast, MCr3 and MCr4, while widely distributed, have been localized in the brain and gut (more on that later). There are also MCr1 broadly distributed in the human body but with functions outside of pigmentation that we are just starting to understand.

For α-MSH, binding to a functional MC1r at the cell membrane causes the α-MSH-MC1r receptor complex to be internalized. That activates a key enzyme within the cell, adenyl cyclase. The activation of adenyl cyclase catalyzes the production of a second signaling molecule called cyclic AMP, or cAMP. The elevated levels of cAMP in turn activates another enzyme, the third signaling molecule, protein kinase A, (PKA). Interacting with other enzymes, PKA then induces the production of melanin as well as enhanced DNA repair and antioxidant enzyme defenses (Figure 4).

## α -MSH (from keratinocytes)

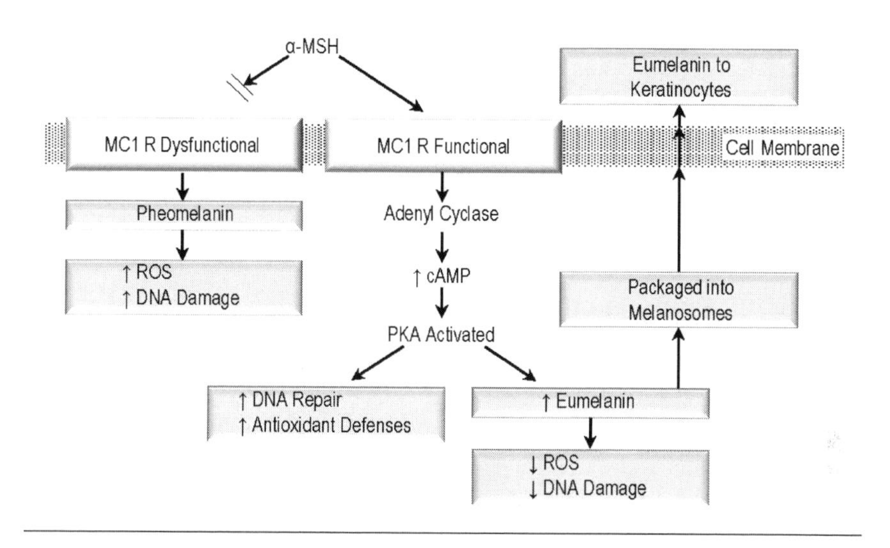


Figure 4: Alpha-MSH (α-MSH) pigmentation signaling in a normal human melanocyte. Alpha-MSH released from sun-damaged K-cells is taken up into the M-cells by a functional melanocortin-1 receptor (MC1r). The complex of MC1r and α-MSH activates the enzyme adenyl cyclase to produce cyclic AMP. The cAMP in turn activates another enzyme, protein kinase A (PKA). The activated PKA then induces both eumelanin synthesis to shield the cell's DNA in the nucleus and increases the ability to repair DNA and reduce oxygen free radical damage.

When scientists studied the MCr1 receptor more closely, they found the usual number of minor genetic alterations with slightly altered DNA bases, mutations or "genetic drift," in different individuals. That is typical of what one sees in all genes when studied across different populations. But the story of MCr1 gene changes became much more interesting when certain MCr1 gene changes could clearly be associated with a higher risk of both non-melanoma skin cancers and melanomas. Some of the MCr1 gene changes were more common in individuals who had developed skin cancers and had a history of poor tanning after sun exposure. Furthermore, many of these same people had red hair and/or prominent freckling. Using gene cloning techniques, it was then shown that M-cells, into which the altered MCr1's were inserted genetically, could not respond to α-MSH by synthesizing the sun-protective form of melanin, eumelanin. So, this suggests that a major mechanism to prevent sunlight-induced skin cancer in humans is having *functional* MCr1, i.e., MC1r receptors that can *respond* to α-MSH and synthesize melanin. With the advent of gene-editing techniques like CRSPR, in the future, we may be able to correct those genetic errors in the MCR1 gene to allow for sun-protective tanning in individuals who cannot appropriately respond to sunlight. Similarly, CRISPR could be used in the future to correct the underlying hemoglobin gene mutations responsible for the different porphyrias, including EPP, afamelanotide's current clinical indication.

If it were just pigmentation, MSH would not be as important in human biology as it actually is. But in addition to tanning, recent studies from Professor Zalfa Abdel-Malek's lab at the University of Cincinnati have shown that MSH also increases DNA repair capacity and the detoxification of oxygen free radicals in M-cells. This makes the peptide hormone α-MSH a much more broad-spectrum protector against both sun damage and cancer formation.

## The Different Melanins

Melanin, from the Greek work for "dark," is an ancient pigmentary molecule which has remained largely unchanged from the spots on dinosaurs, the defensive "ink" of the cephalopods, the cuttlefish and the octopus, the coats of lower mammals, the nose of the dog, and, finally, our skin. Melanin is a long polymer of an oxidized form of the amino acid tyrosine. We can skip the chemical process and go right to the final products: the three basic types of melanin. Eumelanin has two forms, brown and black. This is the type of melanin that has the ability to absorb light energy and dissipate over 99.9 percent of absorbed UV radiation. Pheomelanin is rich in the amino acid cysteine, which is derivatized to a reddish pigment called polybenzothiazine. This is the pigment responsible for red hair and other fair-skinned skin attributes like freckles and moles. The third type of melanin is neuromelanin, found in highest levels in the human brain, but has no role in human tanning.

In certain bacteria and fungi, melanin forms an integral part of their immune defenses, but in humans, the best-described function of melanin is to shield the skin cells from DNA-damaging UVB radiation. Melanin is also found in human hair, the iris of the eye, and in the adrenal glands. The dark brown to black pigment, eumelanin, is the primary form found in human skin and hair. In the hair, very small amounts of brown eumelanin produces blond hair, whereas having a slightly greater amount of black eumelanin produces gray hair, in the absence of other pigments. Eumelanin is also the primary form of melanin that is lost in individuals with albinism. In normal human skin, melanin released from the M-cells is taken up by K-cells to form the cellular nuclear shield, described earlier. It is the primary sun-protectant form of melanin. The reddish colored pheomelanin, on the other hand, does not provide much, if any, sun protection compared to eumelanin. Pheomelanin is structurally different from eumelanin in that pheomelanin has a high sulfur content, which imparts the reddish color. And there are numerous experimental studies that show that when pheomelanin is exposed to UV light, it can stimulate the production of oxygen free radicals, which are very powerful toxins inside a cell. Furthermore, DNA is a common target of oxygen free radicals in cells. This raises the potential that compared to eumelanin, pheomelanin provides much less UV absorption (protection) and may actually *increase* oxidative conditions inside skin cells—a very nasty combination. And individuals with non-functional MC1r from gene alterations tend to produce pheomelanin instead of eumelanin. This helps to explain the coincidence of increased skin cancers and the relative inability in redheads to tan without first burning. It is primarily due to the inability to produce protective eumelanin over the DNA-damaging pheomelanin.

So, to summarize what we know about tanning in humans, all tans in Caucasians are started with UVB damage to the DNA of the outer layer (epidermal) skin cells, the keratinocytes (K-cells). In response to that DNA damage, the K-cells make and release α-MSH, which is taken up into melanocytes by a specific melanocortin-1 receptor (MC1r). The internalized MC1r/α-MSH complex then initiates an enzyme activation cascade leading to the production of the photo-protective dark pigment called eumelanin. To complete the tanning cycle, the M-cells release melanin back to the K-cells to protect their nucleus where the DNA resides. If there is a mutation in the MC1r, such that the M-cells are not properly stimulated by α-MSH, then the M-cells make a reddish type of melanin, pheomelanin. However, that pheomelanin is not photo-protective and may actually increase sun damage.

Finally, to complete this chapter, we have tried to answer a few questions that frequently arise about this science:

## Can afamelanotide be administered by mouth or as a skin cream?

If it were possible to develop this as an oral drug or as a rub-on skin cream, it would make life a lot easier for the patient and for the drug developer. And since the site of the drug action is in the skin, it seems logical to administer as a cream. Further, developing it as a more conventional pill would make it even easier. The short answer to both routes of administration is that the digestive substances in our stomachs would destroy the peptide very quickly, and the molecule is too large to be absorbed across the skin. In addition, both of these routes would make it difficult to control the exact dose administered and would really complicate the FDA regulatory approval route. Administering it as a slow release injectable pellet by the physician in his office gives complete control of the dose, which eases the regulators' concerns.

## Why is a slow release pellet needed rather than a simple injection?

The limited life of the peptide in the blood is also the reason why we cannot simply use α-MSH as the tanning drug. Peptides are broken down and destroyed by natural enzymes in our blood. Scientists refer to the "half-life" of a drug, which is the time for one half of the dose to be destroyed. The half-life of α-MSH is about a minute, so it is very quickly destroyed. One of the main reasons for developing afamelanotide is that its half-life is about thirty minutes, which enables it to circulate in the blood with time to have the desired effect. However, even this extended half-life is not sufficient to get enough of an effect from a single injection, and we found that developing the slow release version had a dramatic effect on the degree of tanning, much more than we expected. In short, releasing a small amount continuously over several days has a much greater effect than a greater amount in a single injection, which is destroyed fairly quickly.

## Is the tan from afamelanotide exactly the same as a natural tan?

Yes, because we are mimicking the natural tanning process. The color and duration of an afamelanotide-induced tan are fully equivalent to a natural sun-induced tan. However, the combination of afamelanotide with a little sunlight greatly increases both the intensity and the duration of the resulting skin tan. We did a lot of work on this and were very gratified with the results. The tan develops quickly and lasts the same amount of time as a natural tan.

# Chapter 15

## *Clinical Trials of Melanotan-1 at the University of Arizona*

**The Skin Cancer Prevention Program Project Grant:** Program Project Grants, or PPGs, are multi-project grants from the NIH that focus on a single area of scientific research. They are organized around a central "theme," the program. The Skin Cancer PPG was originally developed by Dave Alberts, MD, at the Arizona Cancer Center, a Division of the UA College of Medicine. The grant was titled "Chemoprevention of Skin Cancer Program Project." The theme for this grant was the identification of skin cancer pathways and the testing of chemo-preventive agents that could potentially prevent the incidence and severity of non-melanoma skin cancers. These included basal cell and squamous cell carcinomas but not melanomas because there was little knowledge of carcinogenic pathways at that time, the early 1980s. As such, there were four separate scientific projects for the PPG, but for this discussion, we'll only focus on Project 2, which was titled "Clinical Pharmacology of Synthetic Melanotropins as Chemoprevention for Solar Carcinogenesis," headed by myself. The overall goals of this project were to develop the preclinical toxicology data to support an investigator-sponsored IND to allow for initial human trials of MT-I and like compounds as pigmentation agents to prevent skin cancer. I had written the draft of Project 2 while attending the annual weeklong meeting of the American Society of Hospital Pharmacists (ASHP) in New Orleans in December of 1986. I was giving talks on a new anticancer agent for a drug company on the first and last days of the meeting, so I was "stuck" in NOLA for the entire week. The sponsoring drug company had arranged for a palatial room at the prestigious W Hotel. So, I basically had the entire week to get the grant application written, as I did not plan on attending much of the actual meeting. To that end, I had taken about ten pounds of paper copies of background articles that I would need for the grant. Again, remember that there was no internet to access any publications and no personal computers—it was all paper.

I welcomed the time away from all the distractions of the cancer center and, especially, running the outpatient pharmacy operation. The hotel was beautiful, but it occurred to me that I always seemed to get the best accommodations when I traveled alone and almost never when my wife, also a pharmacist, came with me. At any rate, I produced the thirty-five-page written draft of Project 2 with hand-drawn figures and an extensive list of citations over that week. I brought it back to Tucson for the cancer center secretaries to put into the proper grant form and process it through the new DEC (Digital Equipment Company) central computer word processing system. The next hurdle would be the dreaded "site visit"—a virtual gauntlet of in-your-face grant reviewers from across the country. Any and all types of questions and "concerns" are fair game at the site visit.

At these site visits, there are representatives from the sponsoring agency, in this case the National Cancer Institute (NCI), a department of NIH, as well as two primary reviewers for each proposed project. There are also various other reviewers for the scientific core services that are proposed to support the individual scientific projects. A typical review team might comprise ten scientists, one to two administrators from other centers, and one to two representatives of the National Institute of Health, the parent of the other US Government Health Institutes. The reviews for a PPG take place over a three-day period, with the review team working at the hotel the night before the site visit to hone their questions for the next "main" day of presentations and questions. The eight-plus-hour review session starts early the next day at the grant site, in this case, the Arizona Cancer Center auditorium on the UA medical campus in Tucson. Sometimes there are afternoon tours of the facility if it is necessary to see specific equipment or laboratories. On the third day, the review team meets in their hotel conference room where the final critiques are written, discussed, and then scores are voted on for each project. Then, it's a mad dash to the airport for the reviewers to try and get back home before spending a third night away from their homes. It's a very big commitment for both the reviewers and the grant applicants. And the financial stakes for PPGs are written in millions of dollars for a typical four to five-year grant period.

At the time I was a relatively newly minted PhD, and while this was not my first PPG "rodeo," it was certainly the most imposing. The two primary reviewers for Project 2 included a female dermato-pathologist from an Ivy League medical school on the East Coast and a very well respected research dermatologist from a prestigious Midwest university. Each reviewer had both MD and PhD degrees and were well versed in skin cancer biology. Following my twenty-minute summary presentation of the project, it became clear that the woman reviewer loved the project. She was blown away by the slides showing the change of color in frogs and dogs given MT-I. However, the Midwestern reviewer was not impressed. He dogmatically stated that humans lacked the capacity to respond to exogenous hormonal pigmentation signals. In short, nice animal slides, "but it will never work in humans. Humans just don't have the means of responding to a systemic peptide hormone like MT-I." This overarching critique came despite the fact that Professor Aaron Lerner, MD, one of the early "gods" of human pigmentation science, had shown in a 1963 publication that black males could further darken after being given a crude preparation that had native α-MSH in it. Lerner, a distinguished professor at Yale University, had first published the structure of α-MSH in 1957 and later became famous for discovering the pineal gland hormone melatonin, now a common over-the-counter sleep aid that, incidentally, has nothing to do with human pigmentation.

Because of the very negative comments from my second reviewer, I felt that Project 2 was "dead in the water." And I prayed it would not bring down the entire PPG since you cannot get a PPG funded unless each of the proposed projects scores well. But, contrary to my worries, Project 2 scored very well indeed, as did the entire PPG. Importantly, we now had the funds to develop MT-1, file an IND, and then move it into the clinic.

**Topical MT-1**: Since MT-1 is a thirteen-amino acid peptide, we knew at the outset that it would almost certainly require an injectable route of administration. This was because only an injection would avoid the peptide's degradation in the digestive system after oral administration. Similarly, topical administration would be very difficult in trying to push a relatively large molecule through the tough outer skin barrier, the stratum corneum. Nonetheless, we initially chose to evaluate the topical route of administration using two methodologies: a simple cream formulation and, later, using an electrical pulse method called iontophoresis. These topical MT-1 studies were done in normal male volunteers under the auspices of the Investigational New Drug (IND) Application #30,685, granted in 1987 by the FDA Division of Dermatologic and Dental Drug Products. This was two years before we would file the Investigational New Drug Application for testing the drug by injection. But the simplicity of the topical studies, and the extremely low likelihood of causing any toxicity, (and, probably, any significant effects) in the skin satisfied the FDA. The university Human Subjects review panel also voted that the topical MT-1 studies could proceed in a few male volunteers.

For these studies, MT-1 at a high millimolar (mM) concentration was blended into a standard oil-in-water cream formulation, one that is commonly used to deliver sunscreens and corticosteroids, like hydrocortisone, to the skin. There were five male subjects recruited and treated with escalating amounts of topical MT-1 cream applied to the inner forearm areas with placebo cream on the opposite forearm. This constituted the first test of our skin color reflectance instrumentation, the Minolta Chroma Meter. This handheld device can measure skin pigmentation in a much more scientifically valid and precise way compared to simple visual assessments and photography, although we also included photos and visual assessments in all of our trials, just to complete the record. Of interest, the Chroma Meter was not originally developed to be a medical device. Rather, it was produced to help Japanese auto manufacturers precisely control paint colors on new vehicles and prevent color drift from batch to batch and car to car. But it also proved useful for measuring human skin color changes, including the darkening from melanin pigmentation. The Chroma Meter shoots a minute pulse of light energy from a xenon lamp onto the surface to be measured, in this case, the skin. The light signal reflected back into the instrument is then split into three parameters- L, a and b. Natural tanning from UV light is associated with a decrease of the L parameter and an increase in the b parameter. The c parameter is not correlated with skin tone changes, so only the changes in L and b were recorded.

As expected, the topical MT-1 cream had no observable effects in the volunteers, despite pushing the MT-1 concentrations to the limits of the peptide's solubility in the cream base. We then moved on to the iontophoresis method, which uses a small electrical current to move drugs through skin. Iontophoresis is well-understood to reduce skin barriers by ionizing the drug to facilitate transdermal penetration. There were four separate iontophoresis protocols involving over twenty normal male volunteers, but none showed any skin effects of the drug. It was clear that with the means available at that time, topical drug administration of MT-1 was not going to work, and we would need to get authorization to test MT-1 by injection.

**MT-1 by Injection:** We submitted the Investigational New Drug (IND) application to the FDA's Division of Dermatologic and Dental Drug Products on July 24, 1990. After some basic questions were answered on the commercial sourcing of the drug from Bachem's laboratory in California, IND # 35,121 was accepted. This would finally facilitate the first-in-human clinical trials of the super-potent peptide analog of α-MSH, Melanotan-1 (MT-1). The head of the Dermatology Division at UA, Norman Levine, MD, was the principal investigator, or "the PI," for this IND and for all of the clinical trials under that IND authorization. He was also one of the three founders of Melanotan Corporation, as related in Book One. Like the topical studies, the clinical studies of MT-1 by injection would be run at the Dermatology Clinic building, just across the street from the Arizona Cancer Center on the north border of the University of Arizona Medical Center campus. That Medical Center campus is itself almost one mile north of the sprawling UA main campus wherein were situated the labs for Victor Hruby's peptide chemical syntheses and Mac Hadley's frog skin bioassays. This IND submission was a remarkable feat for the team because we had little prior experience developing an IND for an injectable drug. Indeed, the INDs for most injectable drugs are weighty, dense applications that are typically submitted by pharmaceutical companies with deep pockets and even deeper regulatory, preclinical toxicology and clinical development departments.

We had the availability of the Skin Cancer Prevention grant funds to do the work and immediately set out on a step-wise plan to clinically evaluate the new molecule, which was being synthesized at a California facility run by the international company Bachem. That facility was able to do peptide syntheses under the rigorous controls mandated by the FDA's Good Manufacturing Principles, or GMP conditions, which is required for drugs that will be tested in humans. We decided to use a very simple injectable formulation. Each batch of injectable MT-1 would be dissolved in sterile saline and then run through filters that would remove any microorganisms that, however unlikely, might be present. The subcutaneous (SQ) route of administration was chosen since that is how the drug had been administered in the preclinical animal toxicology studies, and there had been no local site complications. Furthermore, the SQ route is well-known for delivering peptides, with insulin being perhaps the best example. And giving the drug by the SQ route also obviates the need for more complicated IV injections. Finally, because the drug is delivered SQ into tissue and not the bloodstream, the effects of a given dose are maintained longer, as the drug slowly diffuses out of the SQ site and into the systemic circulation.

We had only one other but major decision—choosing the starting dose. This is a critical decision with any drug that has never been in humans. Starting with a dose that is too low would mean that many time- and patient-consuming dose-escalations would be required to get to a safe but effective dose. On the other hand, starting with a dose that was too high could cause immediate and unknowable toxicities. We therefore chose to start at half the dose that had been used in the miniature Yucatan pig study, or 0.08 mg/kg/day for ten days, delivered over a twelve-day period. Thus, no doses were given on the intervening weekend when the Dermatology Clinic was closed. This meant that the daily dose for a typical 80 kg adult was about 6.5 mg. This would comprise the first-in-human trial of a super-potent derivative of alpha melanocyte stimulating hormone, MT-I.

There were twenty-eight subjects accrued to the first trial of SQ MT-1, and twenty-six completed the study. All subjects were instructed to liberally use a sunscreen, which was provided at the outset of starting the ten daily MT-1 injections. There were twelve subjects with fair skin (Fitzpatrick scale 1–2), and sixteen with darker skin types (Fitzpatrick scale 3–4). The trial began in April of 1990, and the results were published the next year in the Journal of the American Medical Association, commonly known as "JAMA." The results of both the photography and the Chroma Meter skin reflectance measures were unequivocal—there was significant skin darkening in almost all subjects. But it was a case of "the rich got richer" in that those with intrinsically darker pigmentation visually darkened more after MT-1 than those with lighter skin tones. That being said, however, the lighter-skinned subjects had the largest *percentage* change in pigmentation. In other words, MT-1 had darkened both light- and dark-skinned subjects, but those that had slightly darker skin types to start with developed deeper degrees of enhanced pigmentation. In comparison, the lighter-skin subjects never got as dark but had the biggest pigmentation change from their baseline. The Midwest dermatology expert that reviewed our grant application was wrong—humans can and do respond to an exogenous pigmentary hormonal signal from a derivative of natural α-MSH.

The areas of skin that darkened the greatest in all subjects included the face, neck, arms and upper trunk, all areas of relatively more-dense melanocyte residence. The buttocks, where there are very few melanocytes, did not pigment. And there were side effects. A facial/upper trunk flushing reaction was commonly observed within a few minutes after the SQ injections. In most cases, the flushing was transient, lasting only a few minutes, but it rarely persisted up to one hour after injection. Importantly, there were sequela from these flushing reactions which were highly visible and could even generate warmth to the touch in the affected areas. In addition, there were a few instances of mild nausea reported after the SQ injections at the time of the initial daily injections. But no vomiting occurred at the 0.08mg/kg dose, and no antiemetics ever needed to be administered. In a few other patients, afternoon fatigue was reported, but that too was felt to be both transient and idiosyncratic. This seminal discovery set the groundwork for a subsequent series of small clinical trials to refine the dose, describe the drug's pharmacokinetics, such as the drug's half-life, and determine the optimal duration of dosing. Finally, we did a study of MT-1 combined with some short-timed periods of sun exposures.

**MT-1 Dose Escalation:** In September of 1990, we embarked on a trial to better define the maximally tolerated dose (MTD) of MT-I by the SQ route since we had only evaluated the 0.08 mg/kg/day dose. The design was to continue to use the schedule of ten daily doses delivered over twelve days: five days on, two days off, then another five days on. Since we had clearly shown that there was tanning at the 0.08 mg/kg daily dose, and with minimal side effects, that 0.08 mg/kg dose then became the baseline from which increasingly larger daily doses would be given. The dose escalation method chosen was the Fibonacci sequence formula, named for a famous Italian mathematician born in Pisa in 1170. But the numerical sequence actually appears in the Indian literature as far back as 200 BC. Fibonacci described a sequence of numbers that surprisingly appeared in many mathematics equations and is unexpectedly observed many times in nature, such as the branching of trees and an uncurling fern or the birthrate of rabbit pairs. The sequence runs as: 1, 2, 3, 5, 8, 13, 21, and on. In drug dosing, the Fibonacci sequence has been shown to provide a very useful means of doing dose escalation that both rapidly reaches the MTD but uses the fewest steps, thereby saving both time and patient numbers. For MT-1, the Fibonacci sequence dictated that level one equaled 0.08 mg/kg, and therefore, level two would be 2 x 0.08 or 0.16, level three would be 3 x 0.08 or 0.24 and level four would be 0.4, all in mg/kg/day.

So, the first three subjects on this dose-escalation trial would be administered 0.16 mg/kg/day for ten days, and light reflectance and side effects would be recorded. If there were no serious toxicities, the next three subjects would be administered 0.24 mg/kg/day, and if tolerated, three more subjects would receive 0.4 mg/kg/day, and so on. At the 0.16 mg/kg dose level, the three subjects had similar side effects as at the original 0.08 mg/kg dose level. There were flushing reactions, and skin darkening was clinically evident over the face, neck, and extremities. The next three subjects received the 0.24 mg/kg/day dose, and side effects increased, with complaints of vague "queasiness" and the same flushing reaction. But there was a new complaint of a transient flu-like malaise post-injection. However, there was also a trend towards more substantial tanning at this dose level. It was felt that side effects at the 0.24 mg/kg dose were clearly greater but not yet dose-limiting, so new subjects were recruited for the 0.4 mg/kg dose level. At this dose level, there was frank nausea and some emesis, the latter requiring the administration of antiemetics. The flu-like malaise was also present and seemed to be of greater intensity. Importantly, although it was just a trend, there was no greater tanning observed at this highest dose level.

The conclusion was that tanning had plateaued at the 0.24 mg/Kg dose level, but side effects had increased markedly and were severe at the 0.4 mg/kg dose level. The 0.4 dose level was thereby deemed to be intolerable. And the trend to slightly greater pigmentation at the 0.24 mg/kg dose level did not seem to warrant the increased side effect profile. Therefore, the 0.16 mg/kg dose was determined to be the correct dose for further studies of MT-1 pigmentation administered by the SQ route. That means that a 72 Kg (160 lb.) adult would require a cumulative total of about 115 mg of drug if the daily SQ route were to be used over twelve days. This was the dose used in the early trials until we found that the controlled, slow-release MT-1 formulation had a much more intense tanning effect and so required a much lower dose. The current Scenesse commercial, FDA-approved product contains only 16mg of MT-1 (afamelanotide), about one tenth of the daily injection dose. That 16 mg is delivered in a slowly dissolving implant which slowly releases the drug and greatly augments its biological effects, as we first demonstrated in the hairless guinea pig model.

**MT-1 Combined with Sunlight:** Up to that point, all of our clinical studies of MT-1 had been done in the absence of sun exposure with scrupulous counseling of the subjects to avoid sunlight and liberal dispensing of free sunscreen creams. The clinical team then produced another protocol for the Human Subjects Committee, and they approved a trial of MT-1 with small initial doses of UV-B radiation delivered by a solar simulator. We also started this trial at the lower MT-1 dose of

0.08 mg/kg since we did not know if there would be any toxic synergy when the drug and light exposure were combined. The endpoints for this trial included

(1) observations of systemic tanning by reflectance,
(2) measuring a change in the amount of sunlight tolerated at the UV-B site by measuring each subject's Minimal Erythematous Dose (MED) of UV-B light energy and then the effects of receiving 3 X MED of UV-B, and
(3) the incidence of pathological "sunburn cells" in biopsies of the irradiated site.
(Note that the MED is the amount of UV-B light required to produce a clearly erythematous [reddened] skin site, which will vary from subject to subject at baseline.)

A final endpoint was added:

(4) to evaluate the higher MT-1 dose of 0.16 mg/kg with actual sunlight exposure to half of the back for three to five days at the end of two standard ten-dose SQ administration regimens. This was performed in eight subjects with Fitzpatrick Type III, IV skin. The other half of the back served as the control without sunlight.

Here again, the results, published in 2000, were remarkable. In the first trial at the lower MT-1 dose, tanning was observed in three of four subjects. More importantly, there was a 47 percent reduction in the number of sunburn cells in the skin biopsies from the UV-B sites in the MT-1 group compared to saline-treated control subjects. That was clear evidence of a major protective effect from MT-1 on the damage caused by UV-B exposure. As expected, skin darkening was much greater using the higher MT-1 dose, and the sites that significantly darkened were the forehead, cheek, and scapula. There were also a few instances of nausea and flushing of the face and neck that occurred sporadically immediately after dosing. However, at the sunlight-exposed back sites, the degree of skin darkening was profoundly greater, as compared to the adjacent non-exposed half-back. And it required only a mean of eighty-seven minutes of sun exposure to achieve a perceptible tan at the sun-exposed half back sites. This compared to a mean of 165 minutes of sun exposure for the same effect to be perceived in the sunlight-only control group. Thus, twice as much sun exposure was needed to produce tanning in the sunlight-only control group. That showed us that MT-1 greatly accelerated the effects of sunlight, suggesting a greater than additive, or synergistic effect, of MT-1 combined with sunlight. However, the additive effects of the combination of MT-1 with sunlight continued as we observed that the skin darkening was maintained over a much longer time period in the MT-1 plus sunlight group. Whereas the tanning in the sunlight-only control group had completely faded back to baseline at the seven-week follow-up visit, there was still significant skin darkening present at the sun-exposed back sites at eleven weeks in the MT-1 group. Clearly, the effect of even a small amount of sunlight with MT-1 produced much greater skin darkening and also significantly maintained that darkening over time. Since we had also included standard pathological review of all the skin biopsy specimens, our dermato-pathologist, Jerry Bangert, MD, could find no significant lesions in any of those sites, and most importantly, at those sites receiving three times MED plus MT-1. Thus, the combination of MT-1 plus sunlight was additive or even super-additive (synergistic) at the level of tanning, but it is not toxic to the skin. In the next trial, we would study the effect of MT-1 on the expression of melanin and, specifically, whether the drug was actually enhancing eumelanin levels in the skin.

**MT-I Effects on Eumelanin:** At the time of this study, the only assay for eumelanin and pheomelanin involved a truly tortuous procedure for preparing the skin samples—the Ito oxidation/hydrolysis procedure. Professor Shosuke Ito at Fujita Health University in Aichi, Japan, had published a method for simultaneously detecting the brown pigment eumelanin and the yellowish pigment pheomelanin using oxidation and hydrolysis. Those degradations would reduce the melanins to fragments that could be separated and quantitated using high-performance liquid chromatography (HPLC). My lab had substantial experience using HPLC to detect cancer drug levels in patients, but this was a whole new ballgame. Luckily, I had a superb graduate student in the lab at that time, Katerina Dvorakova, from the Czech Republic. It was clear from reading the papers on the Ito method that the entire procedure depended upon controlling the degree of oxidation of eumelanin using permanganate, and the degree of hydrolysis of pheomelanin using hydriodic acid. Any inconsistency in the percent of melanin degradation in the acid would lead to erroneous results. The final molecules analyzed by HPLC would not be intact melanins rather their degradation products: pyrole-tricarboxylic acid (PTCA) for eumelanin and aminohydroxy-phenylalanine (AHP) for pheomelanin. Since these were extreme chemical degradation procedures, any mistakes would be catastrophic, as the samples would be rendered completely useless for any further analyses. But Katerina was well up to the task, and after many initial and often frustrating "learning experiments," she was able to get consistent PTCA and AHP degradation products from normal skin samples. Now we were ready to test skin samples from subjects treated with MT-1 to document any increases in melanin.

The skin samples for this study were obtained as shave biopsies from six normal volunteers with Fitzpatrick Skin Types III and IV—good tanning skin types. The subjects completed the standard ten-day SQ dosing regimen at 0.16 mg/kg and reflectance measures showed significant tanning. One week later, shave biopsies were taken from the forearm (n = 6) and the forehead (n = 3). Thankfully, the tissue degradations in the hydroiodic acid went smoothly, and we were able to get HPLC analyses performed for both eumelanin and pheomelanin. The results were highly significant: mean PTCA (eumelanin) levels increased by 98 percent in the forearm and 49 percent in the forehead. In contrast, the AHP (pheomelanin) levels did not change from baseline. But importantly, since eumelanin had nearly doubled, the *ratio* of forearm eumelanin to pheomelanin increased from 51:1 at baseline to 86:1 following MT-1 dosing. Thus, MT-1 was clearly inducing skin darkening by enhancing *eumelanin* levels in human skin and without affecting the pheomelanin levels, which remained very low.

**MT-I Pharmacokinetics:** Since the half-life in humans of a crude sample of the natural α-MSH hormone was known to be only one to two minutes at best, we next decided to study the ability of the modified MT-1 peptide to resist the rapid degradation and elimination that happened to the native hormone in human subjects. Professor James Blanchard, a pharmaceutical sciences expert at the UA College of Pharmacy, was recruited to perform a detailed analysis of the disposition of MT-1 by three routes of administration: intravenous (the gold standard), SQ, and oral. The method of detecting MT-I was by a radio-immuno assay, or RIA, which used a radio-labeled antibody that bound to the native α-MSH peptide, but which also bound to and detected the modified alpha-MSH peptide, MT-1.

Three subjects who were finishing the standard ten-day dosing regimen had serial blood and urine samples obtained just before and then following the last, tenth SQ dose of 0.16 mg/kg, and the RIA was used to detect the amount of MT-1 remaining in the blood. Of interest, the blood sample taken just before the last dose was administered had no detectable MT-1, meaning there was no accumulation of drug in the blood from the prior nine doses. In other words, all of the MT-

1 had been cleared from the bloodstream within the preceding twenty-four hours. Importantly, the same total blood levels were present following IV or SQ dosing. This meant that the SQ dose was completely absorbed into the bloodstream, yielding a so-called bioavailability ratio (SQ/IV) of 1.00, indicating 100 percent absorption from the SQ injection site. In contrast, there was no MT-1 detected in blood after oral dosing, which is mostly what we expected. Thus, the drug was completely destroyed in the gut before any absorption into the blood stream could occur. Similarly, less than 1 percent of the dose was detected in the urine, indicating that MT-1 was nearly completely metabolized to inactive fragments, regardless of whether the drug was given IV or SQ. That is also what we anticipated, since peptides are not excreted into the urine in an intact, active form. The one surprising feature that represented a major improvement with MT-1 was the elimination half-life, which is the time the body takes to eliminate one-half of the drug present in the blood. The half-life for SQ-administered MT-1 ranged between 48 minutes and 1.7 hours after SQ dosing, a vast improvement (increased half-life) over the native hormone's one- to two-minute half-life in the blood.

So, the big findings from this study were that MT-1 remained in the blood stream far longer than the native molecule, and all of the drug was absorbed systemically after SQ administration. Indeed, MT-1 blood levels were still detectable for up to 6.5 hours after SQ dosing . In contrast, an earlier published study by other researchers showed that no α-MSH was detectable two minutes after SQ dosing of the native hormone. Clearly, MT-1 was much more resistant to degradation and metabolism compared to the native molecule in vivo. And this had been correctly predicted in studies done by Professor Hadley which showed MT-1 was quite resistant to degradation in biological fluids in vitro. But now we had in vivo proof, and in humans. Overall, this meant that the systemic exposure to a given dose of drug was orders of magnitude greater with MT-1 compared to α-MSH. But even with the extension of the half-life from 2 minutes to up to 102 minutes, the main conclusion of this pharmacokinetic study was that other means of extending the exposure time to MT-1 would probably be needed, i.e., a slow-release depot formulation. The following quotes from Professor Blanchard's summary MT-1 pharmacokinetics report of 1996 "The short half-life also means that relatively frequent doses would need to be given to maintain therapeutic blood levels; hence a DEPOT injectable formulation seems to be a very logical approach." So that became the new search that the team undertook.

**End of Clinical Trials of Melanotropins at the University of Arizona:** On March 11, 1997, we received a letter from the FDA's Division of Dermatologic and Dental Products placing IND 35,121 on a "Clinical Hold" for three deficiencies. These included

1. Reports of alpha MSH affecting melanocyte proliferation and melanoma published from 1990 forward. These had not been addressed since IND 35,121 was originally submitted on July 24, 1990.
2. Two subjects experiencing a stretch-yawn complex after SQ MT-1, that in one case preceded the onset of penile erection. This suggested that MT-1 might be acting in the brain, and there were reports of α-MSH disrupting the blood-brain barrier that needed to be addressed.
3. Published data on immunomodulating effects of α-MSH and, specifically, whether MT-1 might alter the cutaneous immune response.

We had earlier shown that radiolabeled MT-1 did not significantly cross the blood-brain barrier, but the new request wanted actual brain studies. We could not do those types of studies nor were they funded as part of a skin cancer prevention grant. However, the question of melanoma stimulation was still the paramount concern, with the caveat that it is nearly impossible to completely disprove a negative. And that is especially the case with a new drug that has "melanocyte stimulation" in its name. But the question of skin cancer development still had to be answered, or the drug was dead going forward. So, using funds from the Columbine Venture Capital investment in Melanotan Corp. USA, we did endeavor to more comprehensively answer that over-arching concern but not in humans. These studies would have to be done in vitro and in animal carcinogenesis models.

By this time in early 1997, we had conducted five major protocols with approximately sixty-four subjects who received SQ MT-1. Another twenty-five subjects had received topical MT-1, but to no avail. Through all of this, Dermatology Dept. research assistant Chris Brooks had done a magnificent job of shepherding the reams of clinical protocols, human subject approvals, study data, and consent forms to get the studies completed. She coordinated accruing the patients and collecting the clinical data. Our principal investigator, Norman Levine, MD, had maintained our study in good standing with the FDA up to the clinical hold letter from the FDA, wherein there was nothing more that we could do with the budget at hand. But the FDA had been fair, even good to us. They had allowed two first-in-class peptide drugs to undergo initial testing in human volunteers (MT-2 development is covered in chapter seventeen). They had monitored our progress and had not raised unreasonable concerns. Indeed, at an early time in our trials, they deferred an on-site inspection by an FDA inspector when I accurately told him we had only treated about five subjects, and there were no other institutions involved in the human trials. Of course, that was after I nearly had heart failure when he flashed his FDA badge and stated he was there to inspect the study results, production batch records, and the safety findings from this and the other participating clinical trial sites.

We had also been able to complete several "value-added" side studies, such as measuring the eumelanin levels and using skin reflectance to more precisely capture the pigmentation changes. Importantly, there had been no serious toxicities in any of the studies, and we had defined the minor side effect profile of MT-1. Transient facial flushing and mild nausea were the main side effects, but they were not dose-limiting and only occurred in some patients, and not after every injection. We had also shown that MT-1 had a much longer half-life in the blood compared to the native hormone. But the drug still needed a more prolonged release profile to extend and thereby amplify the tanning effects. Finally, MT-1 was shown to be safe both alone and when combined with sun exposure. And there was good evidence for tanning synergy when the drug was combined with even small amounts of sunlight.

The March 1997 FDA letter ended the University of Arizona studies of MT-1 in humans. The drug's development then moved to Australia, first under EpiTan and then Clinuvel, who gained FDA approval for the MT-1 implant, now called Scenesse, on October 8, 2019. Approval came first in December of 2014 in Europe under "exceptional conditions" for the EPP indication. And then, finally, it was approved by the FDA in the US five years later. This was where the drug was originally created by graduate student Tomi Sawyer working in Victor Hruby's chemistry lab on the UA main campus. Of note, the approval for US commercialization was granted on October 8, 2019—twenty-eight years after the initial Phase I/II trials of SQ MT-1 were published in the Journal of the American Medical Association. And that was *thirty-nine years* after Tomi Sawyer, Victor Hruby, and Mac Hadley published their seminal work on the drugs' synthesis and initial biological activity in frog skin pigmentation assays in the prestigious journal The Proceedings of the National Academy of Sciences (October, 1980 ; Vol. 77, pages: 5754–5758). Clearly, although this is not unusual for a new drug, that is way too long for a US-discovered drug to make it back into the US market, but that is the not-so-pretty story for MT-1.

# Chapter 16

## *Preclinical Studies with MT-I to Enable Clinical Trials*

*Note that this chapter is highly technical, and was included only for comprehensiveness. But, it is not necessary to be read for the lay understanding of the drug's development. In other words, for the non-scientists, read the conclusion starting on page 161 and then, feel free to "skip ahead".*

**Animal Toxicology Studies:** To support any IND application, two animal toxicology studies are required, and we chose rats and pigs as our two species. Rodents are commonly used in preclinical toxicology studies, but the pigs, actually miniature Yucatan swine, were chosen because pig skin is most similar to human skin. The rat studies were straightforward assessments of acute high doses and chronic lower doses of MT-1, all administered by SQ injection—the same route that we proposed to use in human subjects. The short summary of the rat studies is that none of the acute high doses of up to 65 mg/M2 of body surface area produced any toxic effects on skin, organs, or blood chemistries. A similar lack of any toxicity was noted in the chronic low-dose regimen of thirty daily SQ injections of 0.6mg/kg/day.

In the pig model, five male miniature Yucatan swine weighing an average 27.4 Kg (60 lb.) were first evaluated for the effects of UV-B light to determine each pig's Minimal Erythematous Dose (MED). One pig received saline as a control, and four received MT-1 at 0.16 mg/Kg/day of MT-1 by SQ injections for thirty days. At the end of this period, all five pigs were retested for their tolerance to UV-B light (MED assessment), and skin biopsies were obtained. The pigs were then euthanized to obtain organ samples, including skin, and blood for serum chemistries. The short answer was the same as in the rats—there were no pathologic changes observed in any animal, and all had gained substantial weight over the thirty days, i.e., they were thriving. The only significant finding at the end of this trial was that there was a 30 percent decrease in sunburn cells at the UV-B irradiated sites in three of four MT-1 treated pigs. In contrast, the control pig exhibited a fifteen-fold *increase* in sunburn cells at the UV-B sites at the end of the trial. Thus, MT-1 had protected the pig skin from UV-induced skin damage.

One side note: to get the excitable pigs to be still for the MT-1 dosing and UV-B treatments, we found that offering a handful of candy corn treats calmed the pigs sufficiently to do the treatments. Our clinician, Norman Levine, MD, observed one of the sessions, as he was interested in seeing what a miniature Yucatan pig actually looked like. But when he started to leave the cage, one of his shoes almost came off. We looked down and realized that one of the pigs had neatly eaten the shoelaces off that shoe, and with no one noticing, not even Dr. Levine. Apparently, a little variety in the diet is important for miniature Yucatan pigs.

Overall, we had demonstrated in two species that MT-1 did not cause any acute or chronic toxicities in a range of SQ doses. And those doses far exceeded what we were planning to start our human subjects at. Because the pigs were felt to be the more similar model for humans, we planned to start our human subjects trial at one-half the dose that had been safely administered to the pigs. That meant we would start MT-1 dosing at 0.08 mg/Kg/day for ten days in our human subjects. This was based on the fact that 0.16 mg/Kg/day for *thirty days* had produced no toxicities in the Yucatan swine. In the rats, the difference was even greater since we had administered 0.6 mg/Kg/day for thirty days with no ill effects. Thus, MT-1 appeared to be safe to move into first-in-human clinical trials.

**MT-I Depot Formulation:** Our initial attempt to produce a slow-release "depot" formulation of MT-I used the commercial copolymer (polymer mixture) called Poloxamer 407 (P407). This viscous material has a central unit of propylene glycol which is hydrophobic (water-repelling or oil-like) and is flanked on both sides with about one hundred units of polyethylene glycol (PEG), which are hydrophilic (water-loving) units. Thus, Poloxamer 407 has water-loving and oil-loving components, and as such, it is widely used in cosmetics to dissolve oily ingredients into a water base. Professor Jim Blanchard's pharmaceutics team at the UA College of Pharmacy also added a variety of additional components to

P407/MT-I mixtures in a water bath testing apparatus. The slowest MT-I release was observed in P407 combinations with methylcellulose, and those were subsequently tested by intraperitoneal injection into guinea pigs. The results, published in 1996, showed that P407 significantly extended the release time of MT-I in the guinea pigs. However, it was felt that even longer release times might be possible with a more rigid formulation for MT-I, one that would have better resistance to dissolution in vivo.

On that basis, a second MT-I formulation project was instituted using a well-known, more rigid, biodegradable material: poly-(lactic-co-glycolic acid), or PLGA. This material has repeating units of lactic acid and glycolic acid, which can be combined into an infinitely variable ratio of the two acids to change the rate of biodegradation and water solubility. PLGA is very slowly degraded in the body by simple hydrolysis to yield the original glycolic and lactic acids. Those simple organic acids are in turn metabolized in the tricarboxylic acid cycle and are eliminated as carbon dioxide and water, making the PLGA polymer safe since it degrades into natural materials. PLGA is also used to provide the slow-release formulation of the prostate cancer peptide drug leuprolide (Lupron), which like MT-1 also contains a D-amino acid substitution to resist degradation. Of note, the 1977 Nobel Prize in Physiology or Medicine was awarded to the discoverer of the peptide drug leuprolide, Professor Andrew Schally.

The PLGA copolymers are produced in a very straightforward fashion. This involves weighing the two acids to the desired ratio and then pulverizing them with a mortar and pestle into a fine powder. That PLGA fine powder can then be mixed with the powdered MT-I, and this mixture is loaded into a tubular mold. The mold is then heated in a controlled fashion to melt the PLGA at temperatures that do not significantly affect the MT-I. Once melted, the mixture is allowed to cool and is then extruded from the mold as a tiny "tube" of drug-PGLA product. The key to this process is to get an even distribution of the drug throughout the melted PLGA such that the amount of drug on the surface is the same as in the interior. This assures a slow but even release of drug once placed in vivo. Having too much drug on the surface leads to a relative "burst" of drug from the formulation just after it is implanted.

The results showed that the best mixture of the PLGA polymer acids was a simple 50:50 combination of lactic and glycolic acids. The extruded final product had a diameter of 2 millimeters (mm) and a length of 8-10 mm containing about

4 mg of MT-I. Scanning electron microscopy was used to visualize the surface of the product to make sure there were no large unfilled pockets and there was a smooth surface structure. Then the products were tested in vitro to characterize the degradation process and monitor the release of drug and the hydrolysis of the PLGA polymer. The results showed that it took about twelve days for 50 percent of the PLGA mass to erode and that there was a "burst" of initial MT-I release followed by a much slower release pattern over several weeks. Now it was time to test the products in the guinea pigs. SQ implantation of the PLGA-MT-I doses was performed after the drug tubes were sterilized by Cobalt-60 irradiation at an outside facility. The hairless guinea pig model was selected because drug release could be measured in blood samples, and pigmentation could be evaluated visually and by reflectance measures. The results, published in 1998, showed that MT-I release from the PLGA depot extended over one month, far surpassing the one-hour half-life seen with the simple saline formulations used in the initial clinical trials of MT-I.

In order to better determine the biological effects of the PLGA/MT-I implants, a second guinea pig study was performed with skin biopsies obtained to measure the amounts of eumelanin in the skin after dosing. These results, published in May of 2000, were, frankly, spectacular. The MT-I released from the implants into the guinea pig's blood tested 100 percent active in the frog skin bioassay and was in an intact form as measured in HPLC assays of drug content. But more importantly, the skin samples, measured by a pyrole-tricarboxylic acid HPLC assay method (described in chapter fifteen), showed a 2.5-fold increase in the eumelanin concentrations *one month* after implantation. Even more spectacular were the visual observations of skin tanning. The guinea pigs were very deeply pigmented at one month to a far greater degree than that seen with SQ injections of much larger MT-I doses in saline. But the big surprise was that significant pigmentation lasted up to *three months* after a single PLGA/MT-I implantation!

These studies proved what we had all been thinking—the way to get the most bang for the buck from a given dose of MT-1 was to deliver it in a slow-release depot formulation. And the 50:50 lactic/glycolic acid PLGA mixture had performed magnificently in vivo. There was no local site irritation, and there was reproducible slow release of MT-1 over one month with biological effects extending out to three months. The degree of pigmentation and its extremely prolonged duration showed us that MT-1, similar to most other hormonal agents, was most effective when formulated to produce a long-lasting exposure rather than as a single SQ injection. Clearly, this was how the drug needed to be evaluated in any future clinical trials of MT-1.

**Carcinogenesis Studies:** The single biggest impediment we faced in developing MT-1 was the overarching concern that it could cause cancer and, specifically, the deadliest type of skin cancer, melanoma. This belief, unanchored by any real scientific observations, caused numerous potential licensees of MT-1 to walk away from the opportunity. In one presentation at Upjohn's headquarters in Kalamazoo, MI, the company reviewer said: "It's right there in the name: alpha-*melanocyte stimulating* hormone." This concern had to be tested, even though we knew it would be hard to dissuade negative "beliefs" about what a superpotent form of α-MSH *might* do.

**Carcinogenesis with Native α-MSH:** Before MT-1 had been invented, researchers had evaluated the natural α-MSH hormone in human melanoma cell lines. In 1973 John Pawelek's lab at Yale University had shown that α-MSH caused the Cloudman S91 melanoma cell line to change shape and appearance, so-called differentiation, into more normal-looking melanocytes. In addition, α-MSH reduced both DNA synthesis and cell counts, i.e., it *inhibited* cell growth. In 1977 studies by Yale University researchers Ruth Halaband and Aaron Lerner similarly showed that the inhibition of melanoma cell growth induced by α-MSH involved the activation of cyclic-AMP, the second messenger for the hormone's activation of the pigmentation pathway. They postulated that the increased tyrosinase activity caused by c-Amp caused the production of damaging oxygen free radicals.

**Melanoma Colony Formation in Soft Agar and in Mice:** Frank Meyskens, MD, at UA showed that α-MSH *reduced* DNA synthesis and colony formation using melanoma samples freshly harvested from patients. There was also a confusing result from the same group seen in Cloudman S91 melanoma colony formation based on the plating density of the melanoma cells. At high plating densities, α-MSH and MT-1 were inhibitory towards colony formation. In contrast, at low plating densities, α-MSH and MT-1 were slightly stimulatory for colony formation. The same dependency on plating density was reported from the Arizona group for human melanoma cells exposed to MT-1 continuously for three days (Jiang et al, 1995).

**MT-1 in a Mouse Model:** In DBA/2J mice injected with melanomas into the front flank, another Arizona research group reported that MT-1 slightly increased the size of the primary flank tumors. However, there were no effects on the number of lung metastases nor on overall survival. The conclusion was that MT-1 was not affecting the overall tumor burden in the mice (Gehlsen et al, Pigment Cell Res, 1992).

**MT-1 Carcinogenesis Studies from Melanotan Corp. USA:** The prior published studies formed the backdrop for a more extensive evaluation of the carcinogenic potential of MT-1, both in vitro and in vivo. This work would be funded by the newly formed Melanotan Corp. USA, a consortium of the UA MT-1 research group, and the Scottsdale, AZ-based venture capital firm Columbine Ventures, headed by Terry Winters, PhD. The resulting studies have not been scientifically reviewed for publication.

**MT-1 with Fresh Human Melanoma Cells in Soft Agar:** There were two objectives for these studies, which were performed by Daniel Von Hoff's group at the Institute for Drug Development in San Antonio, TX, in 1998:

1. Does MT-1 alter melanoma colony formation in a dose-dependent fashion?
2. Can MT-1 stimulate colony formation with normal epidermal melanocytes?

The sixteen melanoma specimens were harvested from melanoma patient tumor biopsies, either primary lesions or metastatic sites. The method involved incubating the freshly harvested melanoma cells with very high concentrations of MT-1 for fourteen days. The number of colonies would then be counted and compared to the number of colonies in the untreated controls. The mean colony counts for cells treated with 0.1 millimolar (mM) of MT-1 was 101.2 percent of control, and 89.9 percent of control for those exposed to 1.0 mM of MT-1. Thus, MT-1 did not stimulate melanoma colony formation and may have slightly reduced it.

To address the second aim, normal (non-cancerous) human epidermal melanocytes were plated in agar and exposed to the same concentrations of MT-1 by continuous exposure over fourteen days of incubation in soft agar. As expected, there were no colonies formed in the untreated control plates. Similarly, no colonies formed in the MT-1 treated plates. The conclusion was that MT-1 does not promote the tumor-like quality of forming large clusters of cells (colonies) in normal human melanocytes. Overall, MT-1 did not affect human tumor colony formation in both established melanomas nor from normal epidermal melanocytes. Next, we evaluated MT-1 in animal models of carcinogenesis.

**MT-1 and Melanoma Tumors in Mice:** Two mouse models were used to address the question of whether MT-1, administered to mice, could cause melanoma tumors to arise or stimulate existing melanoma tumors. In the latter model, Professor Tony Thody, at the University of Newcastle upon Tyne, had previously reported that MT-1 did not stimulate the growth of Cloudman S-91 melanomas growing in DBA/2J mice (Hunt et al, 1993). I repeated that type of study in C57/Black mice harboring B-16 melanoma tumors in their front flank. The results showed no effect of MT-1 doses of up to 1 mg/kg on B-16 melanoma growth over a sixteen-day time period. At the end of that period, all of the MT-1 treated mice had tumor sizes comparable to the untreated control mice.

**MT-1 in SCID Mice:** The next model we tested was much more elaborate, involving the use of special mice that are genetically modified to accept human tumor implants. Mice with Severe Combined Immunodeficiency (SCID) have weakened immune systems that allow human tumors to grow. Five different human melanoma tumor cell lines were implanted in five sets of SCID mice, and MT-1 was administered by the intra-peritoneal injection route. The results showed no effects of MT-1 on the growth of any of the five human melanoma cell lines. We performed a further experiment in SCID mice asking the question of whether MT-1 could cause normal human epidermal melanocytes (NHEM) to form tumors in vivo. This was testing the hypothesis that perhaps MT-1 could *transform* NHEM's, which are non-tumor forming, into malignant melanocytes that can form tumors in the SCID mouse model. In these studies, NHEMs were first grown in vitro in a high concentration of one micromolar (1 uM) of MT-1 to try and induce a malignant transformation. Those MT-1-exposed NHEM's were then harvested and implanted into the SCID mice. The results showed that MT-1 did not cause a malignant transformation of NHEM's into tumor-forming melanocytes, i.e., there were no tumors formed in both the control mice given NHEMs nor in those given NHEM's previously exposed to MT-1.

**Transgenic Mouse Studies:** A final mouse model used another type of genetically modified mouse to evaluate the effects of topical MT-1 on the formation of papilloma tumors in the skin. Transgenic mice are genetically modified as embryos to incorporate human tumor-generating (oncogenic) genes into their genome. In our case, we used mice that had incorporated one of two well-known oncogenic genes for human tumor formation: *H-Ras* and *v-Jun.* The hypothesis being tested with these transgenic mice was whether MT-1 could *initiate* tumor formation in a two-stage model of cancer progression involving initiation (step one), and promotion (step two). These studies were performed by UA alum Marianna Powell, PhD, at her lab at Stanford University in California. The test model involves the topical application of a known cancer-promoting chemical tetra-decanoyl phorbol acetate (TPA), or MT-1, to the skin of the transgenic mice for eight weeks who are then followed for twenty weeks to observe any tumor formation at the application sites. As expected, the TPA-treated (positive control) mice did develop multiple papilloma tumors on their back at the site of TPA application. This was noted at week seventeen in both mouse control groups harboring either the *H-Ras* or the *v-Jun* transgenes. In contrast, there were no papillomas observed in either transgene mouse group treated with topical MT-1. In addition, the *v-Jun* mouse group demonstrated clearly visible pigmentation at the MT-1 treatment site, indicating a biologic response to the MT-1 applications. Further follow-up in that group also showed diffuse coat color darkening. In the *Ras* mice, darkening from MT-1 was not apparent since those mice have intrinsically darkened skin and coat colors.

**Carcinogenesis Conclusions:** Despite the major *a priori* concerns about cancer causation with MT-1, we were not able to demonstrate any effects on tumor formation or growth in any of the numerous preclinical cancer models we evaluated. And this does make biological sense in that no other natural human hormones have been demonstrated to be cancer-causing. The fact that MT-1 is vastly more potent than α-MSH did not matter in these cancer models. And, if anything, MT-1 was shown to be inhibitory in mouse melanoma cells tested in vitro. From a biological standpoint, MT-1, like the native hormone α-MSH, are *differentiating* molecules, a conclusion that John Pawelek had expressed for α-MSH in 1973. By this, he meant that these melanotropic peptide hormones cause melanocytes to become more functional and, importantly, to not revert to a more primitive and proliferative state.

In addition to the mouse melanoma cell studies, there were no effects of MT-1 in freshly harvested human melanoma cells growing in soft agar. Similarly, we could show no effects on tumor growth in vivo, whether in mouse tumors or in human tumors evaluated in two types of genetically modified mice.

The problem we faced is that it is extremely difficult to totally disprove a negative proposition. How do you really know what a new chemical entity will do in humans before it is actually tested in humans? That worry, despite a complete dearth of evidence, significantly held back the clinical development of both MT-

1 and MT-2, and for a substantial period. But now, with the arc of time and experience in our favor, we can see that the preclinical data was accurate. No effects of MT-1 or MT-2 on cancer have been observed over many years and with many hundreds of human patients treated. In this case, humans validated the mouse studies.

# Chapter 17

## *Melanotan-2 (MT-2)*

***Note that this is also a highly-technical chapter and can easily be bypassed for the non-scientist reader.***

MT-2 was the product of a concentrated effort to define the minimal number and sequence of amino acids that were required to maintain activation of the MC1r and pigmentation. Thus, the Hruby lab had been synthesizing smaller versions of the linear thirteen-amino acid peptide MT-1, which were then tested for pigmentary potency in the frog skin bioassay in the Hadley biology lab. These studies showed that amino acids at both the carboxyl (C-terminal) and the amine (N-terminal) ends of the thirteen-mer peptide, afamelanotide, could be cleaved off and still yield an MT-1 fragment molecule that was active at inducing pigmentation. Importantly, the backbone of all of these shortened peptides contained the crucial D-phenylalanine in the center (D-Phe 7) since that substitution was known to be crucial for maintaining pigmentation superpotency. Moreover, structural studies of the D-Phe 7 substitution in MT-1 clearly showed that this D-Phe7 change was "bending" the otherwise linear peptide into a roughly U-shaped configuration, with D-Phe 7 at the base of the "U." This further strengthened the proposition that the N and C-terminal amino acids were not participating strongly in the binding interaction between the drug and the MC1r.

Most of these MT-1 fragments had been developed by an Iraqi graduate chemistry student in the Hruby lab, Fahad Al-Obeidi, who took over after Tomi Sawyer's pioneering work and PhD graduation. Fahad had an amazing story of how he came to the Hruby lab in the late 1980s from Iraq, which at the time was locked in vicious unending combat with Iran. The Iraq-Iran War had become a virtual meat grinder of young men on both sides. Fahad, who held an Iraqi pharmacy undergraduate degree and an MS in physical chemistry, had been drafted into the Iraqi Army and was serving as a medic, albeit in a city army hospital. But the need for battlefield medics was almost sure to call him to the front at any moment. Following his MS degree, he had applied several times for a US student visa without a positive response. But then, out of the blue, he was accepted and a sponsorship through the University of Arizona was put in place. But would Iraq essentially let him go in the midst of an all-consuming war? It was not clear how or why, but the Iraqi authorities relented, and he was off to Tucson, AZ, and the University of Arizona chemistry lab of Victor Hruby.

Entering the lab, Victor offered a project for any of the new grad students to form a closer liaison with the medical team on the health sciences campus that was then clinically testing MT-1. Fahad eagerly took that assignment and started participating in joint chemistry/medical working group meetings. After several of these meetings and great discussion, it was determined that the next project for the skin cancer prevention grant would involve the selection and preclinical development of one of the MT-1 fragments. The aim would be identical to the development of MT-1, only this time we had a considerable group of MT-1 fragments to select from. Working off the hypothesis that the active conformation of MT-1 was a U-shape, and with knowledge that several of the N- and C-terminal amino acids could be left off, a chemical synthesis plan was devised to make an even more stable molecule that retained the D-Phe 7 and decreased the numbers of amino acids at both terminal C- and N-positions. To accomplish that feat, some novel chemistry had to be developed by covalently linking the C- and penultimate N-terminal amino acids. If it could be done, this would yield a "cyclized" peptide with roughly a circular or "O" shape instead of the U-shaped linear peptide MT-1. And because the linkage of the N- and C-terminal amino acids would be covalent, the shortened "cyclized" fragment would be "locked" into the more active conformation for receptor binding.

The ultimate structure of MT-2 had only seven amino acids compared to thirteen with MT-1. It retained the D-Phe substitution and incorporated substantial revisions at both the N- and C-ends, which were now covalently linked together using a lactam bridge. The word *lactam* is a portmanteau of the words *lactone* and *amide.* In chemistry, a lactam is simply a cyclic amide with the general formula of a carbon ring containing three to seven carbons linked together in a cyclic ring melnin

Perhaps one of the best-known lactams that occurs in nature is the beta-lactam ring in the penicillin molecule. Indeed, that lactam ring is often targeted by penicillin-resistant bacteria that produce the degrading (inactivating) enzyme beta-lactamase.

In MT-2 the three N-terminal amino acids in MT-1(Ser-Tyr-Ser) were removed. Instead of Met at position 4 of MT-1, the first two AA's at the N-terminus in MT-2 are norleucine (Nle) and asparagine (Asp). This is followed by the conserved MC1r binding set of four AA's: -His-D-Phe7-Arg-Trp. The C-terminal AA in MT-2 is Lysine (Lys), another substitution from C-terminal AA, Valine, in MT-1 (figure below). As in MT-1, both terminal AA's in MT-2 have modifications: acetylation (Ac) at the N-terminal Nle and amidation (-NH2) at the C-terminal Lys (Figure). These changes yield the following final structure for MT-2, depicted in both the linear drawing compared to MT-1, and in the more accurate cyclized chemical depiction of MT-2

MT-2 Linear depiction, with the conserved receptor binding sequence highlighted

MT-2: Ac-$Nle_1$-$Asp^*{}_2$-**$His_3$-D-$Phe_4$-$Arg_5$-$Trp_6$**-$Lys^*{}_7$-NH2

MT-1: Ac-$Ser_1$-$Tyr_2$-$Ser_3$-$Met_4$-$Glu_5$- **$His_6$-D-$Phe_7$-$Arg_8$-$Trp_9$**-$Gly_{10}$-$Lys_{11}$-$Pro_{12}$-$Val_{13}$-NH2

Figure 5

*Sites for the lactam bridge covalent linkage

## MT-2 Proper Cyclized Chemical Depiction

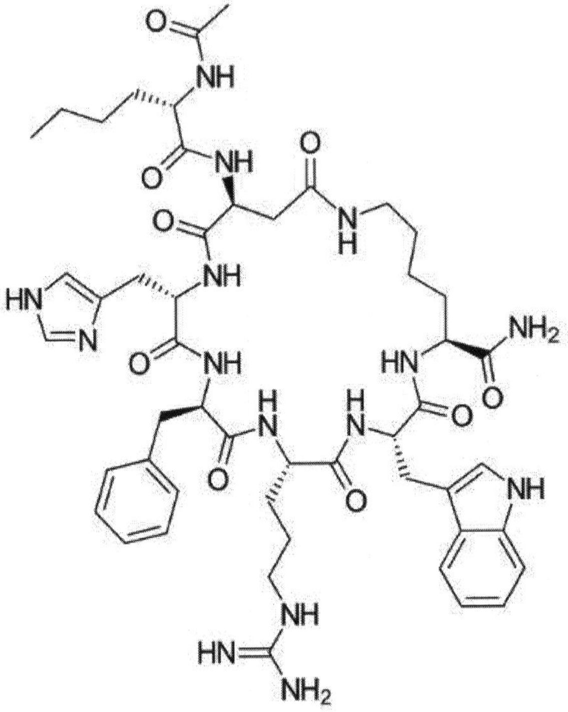

Figure 6

Of all of the Melanotan-1 fragments tested in Mac Hadley's lab, MT-2 looked to be one of the best in terms of potency. It surpassed MT-1 in pigmentation potency in the frog skin bioassay, and the cyclized structure gave it a certain flare for novelty of design. But there was also a projected increase in stability with the cyclization. This was because the two terminal AAs were now covalently linked together and thereby not available to be enzymatically or hydrolytically stripped off as readily as the free AAs in MT-1. The smaller number of amino acids also meant fewer chemical steps needed to be performed to get the final product, a not insignificant benefit since each AA had to be serially added to the chain end while simultaneously chemically blocking all other possible sites of AA addition.

The two groups of the basic scientist chemists in Victor's lab and biologist Mac Hadley decided that MT-2 should be the next candidate for preclinical development as a means of moving to initial clinical testing in human subjects. Of course, Mac short-circuited all of that when he "experimented" by self-dosing MT-2, unbeknownst to the rest of the team. So, we started to put together another Investigational New Drug (IND) application for MT-2. This would require the standard three main components for the eventual FDA review:

(1) the chemistry manufacture and controls (CMC) section,
(2) the preclinical toxicology and pharmacology data, and
(3) the protocol for the planned phase I, dose-escalation trial in human subjects.

The first decision was that because of the special chemistry needed to make the cyclized peptide, the CMC tasks would be performed in Victor Hruby's laboratory on the main UA campus. Protocols for the synthesis and purification of MT-2 were developed and put in place along with the preparation of several test batches of MT-2. Confirmation of the MT-2 final structure after synthesis and purification was performed using both NMR spectroscopy and high-performance liquid chromatography (HPLC). These tests would make sure that we could consistently prepare drug supplies that were pure enough for human use. Those initial batches were also used to perform the required animal toxicology studies.

A thirty-day toxicology study was performed in Sprague-Dawley rats given MT-2 by the oral and subcutaneous (SQ) routes of administration. At the end of thirty days of daily dosing, all of the rats were alive and had gained weight, similar to the placebo-treated controls. The rats were then sacrificed, and the organs harvested for histopathological analyses. There were no significant toxicology findings in the rats. Other tests performed at that same time included a single high-dose SQ injection study in CD-1 male mice. This similarly showed no toxic effects, even with monitoring out to three months after injection. MT-2 was also tested in the Ames in vitro mutagenesis assay. The goal was to see whether MT-2 could induce mutations in two strains of specialized *Salmonella Typhimurium* bacteria that have genetic defects to determine whether an agent is capable of producing genetic mutations. MT-2 was non-mutagenic in both strains of bacteria, even at massive drug concentrations of up to one milligram/milliliter (mg/mL). Finally, pharmacokinetic study using the frog skin bioassay in CD-1 mice showed that MT-2 had prolonged blood levels with a half-life of about thirty-six hours. These studies were completed in April of 1991.

One of the key preclinical findings with MT-2 was that radiolabeled drug was detected in rat brains after SQ dosing. This was a clear contrast with MT-1, which did not cross the blood-brain barrier. And, frankly, we did not understand the significance of that finding until years later.

With the findings of no serious toxicities in the animal studies, a new Investigational New Drug (IND) application was assembled and submitted to the FDA to allow for first-in-human clinical trials (excepting Professor Hadley's unsanctioned experiment with MT-2 on himself). In this case, the drug for the human trials would come directly from the Hruby chemistry lab on the main campus of UA. The final product would be purified by HPLC and characterized for pigmentation effects in the frog skin bioassay in the Hadley lab. This was an enormous benefit to kickstarting the trials because we were not relying on outside vendors. But, conversely, there was similar enormous internal pressure to produce a quality product for the human trials. The FDA again came through for us and approved the IND in 1993, allowing the team to start SQ dosing in normal male volunteers. A standard dose-escalation scheme was used, but due to the enhanced potency over MT-1 in the bioassays, a much smaller initial dose was selected—only ten micrograms/Kg of body weight and next-dose increments using the same Fibonacchi dose escalation scheme as used for MT-1. On alternating days, the subjects would receive either MT-2 or saline as a means of discerning that any acute effects were from the drug and not the injection procedure itself. The dosing period was Monday–Friday (five injections/week) for two weeks (ten injections).

The results of this small trial were published in the journal *Life Sciences* in 1996, and the findings did not disappoint—MT-2 was clearly much more potent in humans than MT-1. Mac Hadley's frog skin bioassays were correct. Mild acute effects of MT-2 in three initial volunteers were noted at the starting dose level, but they did not limit dose escalation. This allowed for daily SQ doses to be escalated first to 20 mcg/Kg and then by subsequent 5 mcg/kg increments to 25 mcg/Kg/day (2 subjects) and 30 mcg/kg/day (1 subject). At those higher dose levels, moderate somnolence and fatigue were seen. Mild nausea was also observed at most dose levels but was transient and did not require antiemetic drug treatment. With all doses above 20 mcg/Kg/day, a stretching/yawning complex was observed a few minutes after dosing. This correlated with spontaneous penile erections, which lasted on and off for one to five hours after dosing. So, Mac Hadley's impromptu experiment had correctly predicted that MT-2 did produce long duration penile erections, and in a predictable pattern. At all doses above the starting dose, all of the subjects showed skin pigmentation one week after dosing ended. MT-2 was a dual-action drug: it tanned and induced penile erections. Because of more severe nausea at the 30 mcg/Kg/day dose, the recommended dose for further trials of MT-2 was 25 mcg/kg/day.

The next logical step would be to test whether MT-2 could perform similarly in men with erectile dysfunction (ED), and we petitioned the FDA for permission to do those studies. After some discussion, it was decided that MT-2 could not be studied in men with ED under the current pigmentation-related approval. In this case, another IND would need to be submitted to the FDA's Division of Metabolism and Endocrine Products, which included urologic drugs. Because this was a far departure from dermatology, we recruited a junior faculty member of the UA's urology group, Hunter Wessels, MD. And after getting yet another IND from the different FDA division, Dr. Wessels did a terrific job of setting up MT-2 trials in men with ED.

The studies in ED proceeded well under Dr. Wessels, and there was no shortage of potential subjects. The protocols called for use of pressure measuring device, a plethysmograph called the Rigi Scan$^{R}$. That device measures penile tumescence at the tip and base of the penis and the numeric results are recorded for later analysis. In one trial, MT-2 was able to induce meaningful and long-lasting erection in seventeen of twenty men with both psychogenic and organic types of ED. There was the same stretch-yawn syndrome, and the onset of significant tumescence ranged from thirty minutes to two hours, with milder tumescence lasting up to three to five hours after SQ injection. About 20 percent of men experienced some degree of transient nausea which did not require drug treatment. But nausea was more severe in a smaller subset of men given MT-2. And yes, there were also pigmentation changes depending on the frequency of MT-2 dosing.

At this point, it is important to explain that the erectogenic effects of MT-2 are not caused by direct dilation of the blood vessels in the penis, which is the mechanism of action for drugs like Viagra (sildenafil). Sildenafil and other oral small molecule ED drugs inhibit an enzyme called phosphodiesterase 5 (PDE5). PDE5 inhibition causes a blood vessel dilator molecule (cGMP) to be protected from degradation. As the levels of cGMP increase after sildenafil, more blood becomes trapped in the corpus cavernosum of the penis and voila, you get an erection. Instead of directly stimulating blood flow in the penis, MT-2 and the latter MT-2 analog, bremelanotide (Vyleesi, Palatin Technologies), cause penile erections by stimulating the centers in the *brain* that induce erections. So, another old adage is true—the brain is clearly the "sexiest organ in your body." And with this central pathway of brain-sex stimulation, females can and do respond.

Of note, Vyleesi and MT-2 are nearly identical molecules. Bremelanotide is simply an active metabolite of MT-2 which lacks the amide at the carboxyl end of MT-2. Bremelanotide had been the product of one of Victor Hruby's postdoctoral peptide chemistry researchers who left Tucson and came to work at Palatin Technologies in New Jersey. And although extremely similar, the two molecules, MT-2 and bremelanotide, are not identical. Thus, after an arbitration hearing between Palatin Technologies and the University of Arizona's patent broker, bremelanotide was ruled to be a unique molecular entity, owned entirely by Palatin Technologies. Like MT-2, bremelanotide is a cyclic, seven-amino acid peptide. The smaller molecular size of seven amino acids in MT-2 and bremelanotide versus the thirteen amino acids in MT-1, and the cyclic shape of MT-2 and bremelanotide versus the linear peptide MT-1, allow for MT-2 and bremelanotdie to penetrate into the brain. And like MT-1 and MT-2, it is not specific for a particular melanocortin receptor subtype. All three peptides, MT-1, MT-2, and bremelanotdie, are non-specific; they stimulate four of the five melanocortin receptors, all except the MC2r receptor for ACTH. But the effects of both MT-2 and Vyleesi on the brain are due to one specific melanocortin receptor, MC4r, which is found in many brain areas and especially in the hypothalamus.

The hypothalamus is an almond-shaped region at the base of the brain, near the pituitary. Its main function is to link the nervous system with the endocrine system, primarily by using specific neurohormones to influence the pituitary. As such, the hypothalamus is responsible for many basic body functions such as regulating temperature and metabolism and also many so-called "behaviors," such as sleep, eating, and, as we now know, sexual arousal. In the hypothalamus, MT-2 and bremelanotide bind to MC4r and cause the release of the neurotransmitter dopamine. Dopamine is well known as a general brain-based mediator of pleasure. Dopamine release in the hypothalamus following MC4r stimulation by MT-2 and bremelanotide induces a sexual signal in the brain. That signal cascades locally to other brain areas and, systemically, to the genitals, leading to both erectogenesis in men and feelings of sexual desire and satisfaction in women. Thus, in late 2019, the FDA approved Vyleesi as a self-administered SQ injection for treating hypoactive sexual desire disorder in premenopausal women.

The acute GI effects of MT-2 were subsequently shown to be associated with weight loss in chronically dosed animal studies. Thereafter, several drug companies, including Merck, went on a huge development effort to find a MT-2-like molecule that reliably and safely caused weight loss. That search produced hundreds of compounds, but no specific weight loss molecule could be identified. And once the lay press learned of the combined effects MT-2, the drug was immediately and, unfortunately, labelled to be "the Barbie Drug." The name was due to the fact it could cause skin tans, erections, and, potentially, weight loss, a continuing Holy Grail in drug discovery. MT-2 even appeared as a headline story in the June 1992 *Vogue* journal with model Claudia Schiffer on the cover. Of note, illicit sales and use of MT-2 is rampant across the internet, with many suppliers hawking highly dubious products. Buyers beware.

As the skin cancer prevention grant period ran out for this project in the mid-1990s, further development of MT-2 at UA essentially stopped. And although we sought several drug company licensees, a deal for MT-2 was never reached. But overall, we had done the impossible. The team had taken two novel peptide drugs through preclinical development and early-stage clinical development. At the time, such "in-house" drug development at a single university was practically unheard of. And we had done all that with very little funding. Clearly, the NIH got their money's worth from that skin cancer prevention grant. Two new molecules were now ready for more detailed clinical development. And we had discovered an entirely unexpected effect of a melanotropic peptide stimulation: sexual stimulation in the brain. Most importantly, we had shown how to pharmacologically short circuit the primordial human tanning cycle initiated by sun damage. Initiating sun-induced DNA damage to keratinocytes was no longer needed for tanning if MT-1 or MT-2 was administered to the person. So, with MT-1 and MT-2, a person desiring sun protection just needed to have functional melanocortin-1 receptors in the skin, and the melanotropic peptide drugs could do the rest.

# Chapter 18

## *Future Medical Applications of Melanotropins*

### Afamelanotide in Other Skin Diseases

**Vitiligo:** Two small clinical trials of afamelanotide (Scenesse) with UV-B light exposure have been published in patients with the disfiguring skin depigmentation condition of vitiligo. Perhaps the most famous vitiligo case in the US was pop singer Michael Jackson, who chose to further depigment the *non*-vitiligo skin areas using a bleaching agent. This may well have been due to fact that there are no robustly effective treatments to re-pigment those whitish vitiligo skin patches. In many African and Asian cultures, individuals with vitiligo are shunned as if they harbored a visible evil. Because the visual effects are so stark, many individuals with vitiligo can be depressed and socially ostracized, although that is improving.

There are many theories about the cause of vitiligo, but the main reason is an immune attack and loss of cutaneous melanocytes in the areas of vitiligo. In addition, individuals with vitiligo have very low levels of α-MSH in their blood, supporting a theory that without sufficient α-MSH, skin melanocytes become weakened and diminished in number, making them more susceptible to immune destruction. Attempts to re-pigment the vitiligous areas have been difficult since there are no melanocytes left to stimulate in the affected vitiligo areas. That is the reason the UA team did not test MT-1 in subjects with vitiligo—we believed it could not work, but we were wrong.

Among the current treatments for vitiligo, none are permanent, and none work well in all patients or body areas. Current treatments for vitiligo include topical corticosteroids and oral immunosuppressant drugs, like cyclosporin, that inhibit calcineurin and narrow-band UV-B (NB-UVB) phototherapy involving light emissions at 311nm. These NB-UVB phototherapy treatments typically involve two to three light exposure sessions weekly for months, which are very inconvenient.

Because of the potential role of below-normal levels of α-MSH in causing vitiligo, a pilot trial was performed at three US-based university dermatology centers and one in France. The study randomly assigned patients with vitiligo affecting 15–50 percent of their total skin area to NB-UVB for one month followed by continued NB-UV-B alone or combined with one afamelanotide 16 mg implant, given monthly for four months (Pearl E Grimes et al, JAMA 149(11):68–73, Jan 2013). While the larger results in fifty-six vitiligo patients have yet to be published, four cases were reported in 2013, and the results were spectacular. In each case, there was a rapid and deeper skin re-pigmentation seen with the addition of afamelanotide. As expected, the non-vitiligo areas of skin also darkened, but the stark contrast of white and dark skin was nearly eliminated. The pattern of re-pigmentation was also significant. It started around the hair follicles and then radiated outward—a classic follicular stimulation pattern. In short, afamelanotide was stimulating inactive melanocytes in the hair follicles. Those still-functional "reserve" melanocytes were stimulated to disperse melnin from the hair root to provide it to the vitiligo skin areas.

A second pilot trial was performed in eighteen Asian vitiligo patients in Singapore who received NB-UVB and six monthly placebo implants versus NB-UVB plus the afamelanotide implants. The results were similarly graphic—the areas of vitiligo became significantly darker with the combination therapy (JJH Toh et al, J Acad Derm, 2020). However, recruitment to the combination arm was limited due to subjects withdrawing, as they experienced the generalized skin darkening that was seen in the previous study. Clinuvel is planning a large US phase III clinical trial of afamelanotide and NB-UVB to start in late 2020/early 2021, in consultation with the FDA.

**Variegate Porphyria:** Afamelanotide is also being investigated as a treatment for other forms of porphyria, including variegate porphyria (VP). VP is caused by an abnormal porphyrin that differs from the porphyrin in EPP patients. But, like the case in EPP, the abnormal porphyrin in VP also causes intense sensitivity to sunlight exposure, leading to pain and blisters as in EPP. Afamelanotide should be able to induce sufficient pigmentation to block the effects of sunlight in VP patients, as it does in patients with EPP. These studies are just beginning with Scenesse in VP patients.

**Hailey-Hailey Disease (HHD):** This disorder was previously known as benign familial pemphigus, a skin disorder characterized by the formation of blisters in the skin and particularly at areas of skin fold (intertriginous areas). Keratinocyte skin cells in patients with HHD have defects in detoxifying oxygen free radicals, which are a direct byproduct of sun exposure. In a pilot clinical experience in two HHD patients, afamelanotide was shown to improve skin lesions at thirty days and completely eradicate the HHD lesions at sixty days after Scenesse implant. Further lab studies in HHD cells showed that afamelanotide was reestablishing skin cell levels of a factor called NERF-2, which coordinates the response to oxygen free radicals. Since there are no other effective therapies for HHD, further clinical trials with afamelanotide in HHD are clearly warranted.

**Solar Urticaria:** This skin condition causes chronic phototoxicity characterized by the classic inflammatory skin response of an itch, wheal (swelling), and flare (redness). The reaction typically occurs within minutes of exposure to sunlight. The precise biological cause of solar urticaria is not known, but it appears to involve the inflammatory signaling molecule immunoglobulin E or Ig E. A single implant of Scenesse was evaluated as a preventive for solar urticaria reactions from a controlled UV-light exposure in a phase II trial in five patients. At thirty days after dosing, the patients showed that more UV light was needed to elicit the wheal response, suggesting that the drug had raised the threshold of UV exposure needed for the wheal response to UV light—a protective effect. At sixty days, the amount of skin involved in the wheal response was significantly smaller compared to baseline, again suggesting that Scenesse was increasing the skin's resistance to the toxic effects of UV light. In addition, all subjects had measurable increases in pigmentation.

**Polymorphous Light Eruption:** PMLE is an immune-mediated skin reaction to sunlight, leading to a characteristic rash. The exact cause is unknown, but the condition is considered to be a type of delayed hypersensitivity response to sunlight. The typical onset of rash is hours after sun exposure, and it typically clears after a few days. The usual recommendation is to avoid sunlight, which can be disconcerting for affected individuals, resulting in a decrease in quality of life. Corticosteroids, both oral and topical, can be used to lessen the symptoms of a PMLE flare, but they will not prevent future PMLE events. To prevent PMLE reactions, patients can receive courses of psoralen combined with UV-B exposure before sun exposure. This therapy, which is often abbreviated as "PUVA" regimens, is associated with increased skin pigmentation. This suggested that prophylactic treatment with Scenesse might be effective in preventing PMLE reactions in affected individuals. Therefore, a pilot clinical trial was performed in thirty-six PMLE subjects who were given either a placebo or a single Scenesse implant and then followed for reactions to sunlight. Dermal symptoms were reduced in the group given Scenesse compared to the control group. Further studies appear to be warranted for Scenesse as a preventative for PMLE.

**Acne Vulgaris:** This very common inflammatory skin disorder has many causes and just as many commercial remedies, each with varying degrees of clinical success. A small pilot trial with Scenesse was done in three patients with mild-to-moderate facial acne. Following a single Scenesse 16 mg implant, all subjects experienced positive outcomes, measured at day fifty-six after dosing. These included a significant reduction in the total number of inflammatory lesions (papules, pustules, and nodes) and non-inflammatory lesions (open and closed comedones). These clinical outcomes were also associated with improvements in patient-reported quality-of-life experiences, as measured by a standardized dermatology questionnaire.

**DNA Repair Diseases**: In addition to vitiligo, potential new clinical applications for afamelanotide include diseases characterized by defects in DNA repair, such as the rare genetic condition xeroderma pigmentosum (XP). Patients with XP have defective enzymes that would normally mediate nucleotide excision repair removing damaged DNA bases in the skin. As such, XP patients develop multiple skin cancers with even minimal sunlight exposure, and eventually, they will die from disseminated skin cancer in their third decade of life. Even staying out of the light as much as possible typically delays the onset but not the ultimate outcome in XP patients. Because afamelanotide, and other MC1r-active stimulators, can enhance DNA repair and the detoxification of oxygen free radicals, these agents might be able to significantly reduce the number and severity of skin cancers in XP patients. This could potentially extend XP patient lifespans but would not correct the underlying genetic defect. However, since there are no existing therapies for XP patients, a reduction in skin cancers, if possible, would be a major improvement in these patients' lives.

Clinuvel has recently announced the treatment of one XP patient, although clinical results weren't provided. The company has planned a small pilot trial in six additional XP patients using endpoints of DNA damage in skin biopsies. Similarly, Clinuvel has announced another planned small clinical trial of afemelanotide in subjects with Fitzpatrick type I and II easily burned skin types. The same end-points of DNA damage in skin biopsies before and after UV light exposure will be used. If successful, that would show that individuals with no underlying disease, other than severe sensitivity to sunlight, could benefit from the drug.

**Arterial Ischemic Stroke**

Perhaps the most ambitious clinical trial proposed by Clinuvel is a trial in patients recovering from arterial ischemic stroke (AIS). The proposed scheme is to use a melanotropin in the time after the stroke to prevent damage to cells around the clot that have not already died from the lack of oxygen, the so-called penumbra. The mechanism of action, in this case, is to rely on the anti-inflammatory effects of melanotropins to protect the penumbra brain cells from proceeding to cell death in the days after immediate event. This is a very ambitious proposal since AIS has been a virtual graveyard for drug development. Other than the clot-dissolving drug, tissue plasminogen activator, or TPA, which is only effective in a very short time frame after the event, all other attempts at developing a stroke drug have failed.

## Other melanotropins in clinical trials:

**Palatin Technologies:** There are three novel melanotropic peptides under development by this company including two MCr1-stimulating compounds: PL-8177 and PL-9643. An oral formulation PL-8177 that survives stomach transit that ordinarily destroys peptide-based drugs is entering an early-stage clinical trial in patients with inflammatory bowel disease. This is based on extensive preclinical studies showing marked reduction of colon inflammation in experimental mouse models. Similarly, an ophthalmic (eye) formulation of PL-8177 is being tested in patients with non-infectious uveitis, a potentially blinding inflammation of intraocular tissues.

PL-9643 is a MCr1-stimulating drug which is in preclinical development as a potential treatment for dry eye disease (DED) as well as diabetic retinopathy and macular degeneration. These are clinical conditions that are significant unmet medical needs. Palatin recently released preliminary results of a small clinical trial of PL-9643 in DED patients. While the trial did not meet the primary endpoint of reduced corneal staining, it did show significant symptomatic improvement. Further trials with Pl-9643 are planned. A final preclinical melanocortin under development by Palatin is PL-8905/9610, a MCr4-specific peptide for the treatment of rare genetic and metabolic types of obesity.

In addition to Clinuvel and Palatin Technologies, there are two other companies developing novel melanotropic peptides. Rhythm Pharmaceutical gained FDA approval in November 2020 for setmelanotide, which contains eight amino acids with two D-substitutions including the all-important D-phenylalanine in the center of the molecule. Like bremelanotide (Vyleesi), setmelanotide is a cyclized (nonlinear) peptide, but in this case, it uses a disulfide bond from two cysteines to bridge the two peptide ends together. Setmelanotide has about twenty-fold selectivity for MCr4 over the other melanocortin receptors and does not stimulate MCr2, the ACTH receptor. It has been developed by Rhythm Pharmaceuticals as a treatment for rare forms of genetic obesity in children involving the pro-opiomelanocortin (POMC) gene. The POMC gene encodes for the production of all of the melanocortins. Rare mutations in the POMC gene can cause intense overeating, beginning early in childhood. Genetic obesity can also be caused by a deficiency in the leptin receptor, which is another satiety signaling molecule. Both POMC and leptin deficiencies cause intense overeating due to the loss of the satiety signals from the hypothalamus that normally occur after food intake. POMC and leptin receptor deficiency are both rare conditions that may affect only a few hundred children in the US, but the enormous weight gain poses a major health threat to those children.

In obese animal and human metabolic studies, setmelanotide was shown to increase resting energy expenditure, which suggests the drug may cause weight loss even in subjects without POMC mutations. Phase III clinical trials with setmelanotide have been completed in individuals with obesity related to POMC mutations and Leptin receptor deficiency, which is another satiety signaling pathway. The drug was administered by SQ injections, and it produced statistically significant weight loss of 49 percent in patients under nineteen years of age and 22 percent in patients older than nineteen. Importantly, setmelanotide did not cause elevations in blood pressure, which was the cause of failure for all of the prior MCr4 agents tested as weight loss drugs. It is anticipated that setmelanotide will be reviewed by the FDA for US approval in 2020 with a potential decision by early 2021.

Dersimelagon (MT-7117) is a MCr1-stimulating melanotropic drug which is a non-peptide small molecule under clinical development by Mitsubishi-Tanabe Pharma. As with afamelanotide, the target population for clinical trials is patients with EPP. But with dersimelagon, the drug is administered as oral tablet(s) given for multiple days. The trials with MT-7117 are just getting underway, but oral administration, if effective, could potentially be much more convenient and less costly compared to the Scenesse depot implants.

**New Melanocortin Analogs:** In addition to these new compounds in the clinic, there are two repositories of novel melanotropic peptides that could be developed and advanced into the clinic. This includes entirely new melanotropic compounds from the original Hruby lab at UA, which were developed by chemistry professor Min Ying Cai, PhD, working with Professor Hruby. Another large set of melanotorpic compounds has been synthesized and characterized by Zalfa Abdel-Malek, PhD, at the University of Cincinnati. Note that Zalfa obtained her PhD in Mac Hadley's UA biology laboratory. Of note, she has been the primary publisher on the DNA repair and oxygen free radical strengthening effects of α-MSH and its derivatives, something we did not know about when we started the pigmentation studies. Importantly, most of the compounds in these two repositories are highly specific for individual melanocortin receptors, unlike afamelanotide, which can stimulate four of the five MCr's. That means there are individual melanotropic agents that only target MCr1, MCr3, Mcr4, or MCr5. That had not been possible earlier, but it was achieved through detailed molecular modeling of the individual MCr structures.

## Melanotropins in Other Medical Conditions

Perhaps the biggest emerging story with the melanotropins is the burgeoning experimental discoveries of the role of melanocortin signaling in pathways that are not associated with skin pigmentation or food intake (Table 3). The myriad of potential medical applications for melanocortins is truly staggering and includes effects in experimental models on inflammation, neurodegenerative diseases like Alzheimer's Disease, and perfusion injuries like myocardial infarction and AIS. An entire book could be devoted to detailing these potential effects, but we won't take you there now. However, the role of melanocortins in inflammation has been better studied and support Palatin's trials of novel melanocortins to treat inflammation in the eye (PL-9643) and in the colon (PL-8177). It is now well known that MCr1 and MCr5 are expressed in human immune cells, including monocytes, macrophages, neutrophils, lymphocytes, and mast cells. Stimulation of MCr1 and MCr5 causes inhibition of pro-inflammatory interleukin cytokines (IL's-1, 2, 4, 6, and 13), as well as Tumor Necrosis Factor (TNF)-alpha. And Palatin has shown that their novel melanocortins are active at reducing inflammation in several relevant experimental mouse models.

This is just one example of where the future lies for the melanotropins—a huge vista of new clinical opportunities for therapeutic drug development. And because most of the newer melanotropin derivatives are truly specific for single MCr's, we will finally gain a clearer understanding of why nature split the MCr's into five distinct receptor subtypes. Thus, the future of the melanocortin drugs will certainly blossom into greatly expanded medical indications, and far beyond pigmentation.

## Table 3: Melanotropin Actions in Experimental Biological Systems

| Melanotropin | Biological System | Reported Effects |
| --- | --- | --- |
| α-MSH | Human melanocytes in vitro | Quenched reactive oxygen species Up-regulation of DNA repair enzymes |
| PL-8331 | Scopolamine-induced mouse model | Improved fluorescein (irritation) score |
| PL-833 | Diabetic mouse model | Reduced (inflammatory) VEGF and a-TNF levels Increased IL-10 levels (inflammation resolution) |
| PL-8177 (Topical to eye) | Experimental Auto-immune uveitis (EAU) mouse model | Reduced EAU clinical score (reduced uveitis) with reversed immune cell infiltration |
| PL-8177 (tablet) | Colitis mouse model | Normalizes colon gross pathology |
| α-MSH | Dorsal root ganglia (neuronal) cells | Protection from cisplatin injury Blocks cell death from apoptosis Stimulates neurite formation (nerve growth) |
| α-MSH | Paraventricula rnucleus CNS injections in rodents | Increased blood pressure via MC4r stimulation increased sympathetic nervous system activity |
| α-MSH | Allergic rodent models | Reduced lung edema, deactivates inflammatory genes in lung cells |
| α-MSH | Bleomycin organ fibrosis in lungs | Reduced collagen (fibrosis) accumulation reduced pro-inflammatory cytokines (TNF-a, IL-6) |

| | | |
|---|---|---|
| α-MSH | Acute and chronic Neuro - degeneration rodent models | Enhanced learning and memory protection blocked systemic response to brain injur by MC4r stimulation of the vagal nerve |
| α-MSH | Ischemic injury (stroke) models in rodents | Reduced brain tissue damage due to MC4r stimulation |
| α-MSH | Alzheimer's Disease models in rodents | Neuronal protection by reduced inflammation with memory maintenance for maze runs |

# Epilogue

We hope you have enjoyed this true story about the development of a class of new drugs, exemplified by the tanning drug, afamelanotide.

Drug development is not a predictable, well organized series of events and it is particularly full of surprising twists and turns when you are developing the first of a new class of drugs. It is truly entrepreneurial, even inside a large company, because the usual reaction to something new is a large dose of skepticism that can easily kill the effort. Reactions such as "that can't possibly work" and "it will have a big safety problem" are normal along the development pathway and it takes a committed team to overcome them all or, in many cases, to prove that the skeptics are correct. It is also a lot more difficult when you are doing it in small venture capital funded start-ups that do not have the financing and resources of the big pharmaceutical companies. It is not unusual for the first of a new class of drugs to take 15 or more years to develop to the marketing stage nor for the effort to fail. Add in the time-consuming requirements of the FDA and you now know why successful drugs are so expensive.

Most new drugs are developed in the United States but afamelanotide is the exception that proves the rule. We believe that it is the first drug that was mostly developed in Australia without the help of a major pharmaceutical partner. True, it started life at the University of Arizona, but we could not find the support needed to complete the development in the United States and we must express our appreciation to the highly entrepreneurial, risk-taking public markets of the Australian stock exchange; it is a unique institution. Interestingly, the subsequent drugs in the class for sexual stimulation and appetite suppression are being developed by independent US companies mostly in the US.

Without the US government support of discovery research at the nation's universities and institutions, this drug class would probably still be waiting to be developed and it is a pleasure to express our appreciation and admiration for the kind of research work which is supported by the National Institutes of Health. Much of it has no obvious goal but it turns out to be the source of many successful drugs that have been developed over the last few decades. Few countries can match the fire power and support for discovery research which is nurtured by the NIH. Couple that with a dynamic venture capital community and abundant capital and it is easy to see why the US biotechnology industry is so productive.

Several of the people who were involved with the story have already been profiled in the earlier pages of this book. All of them share a common characteristic of being vitally interested in the development of innovative products and they all had the courage to devote some of the most productive parts of their careers to working on this very fragile concept of a new drug, with the very real risk of failure that comes with it. To all who were associated with this, we extend our thanks and appreciation. It was a pleasure to know you all even though we did not always agree!

The reason we do this kind of work is for the patients. There is no greater experience than to have participated in the development of a drug that will relieve suffering and improve lives. We hope that afamelanotide and its derivatives now under development continue to address significant numbers of patients and help to relieve troublesome conditions and symptoms.

We have shown you that the afamelanotide story is an incredibly long tale of drug development, full of twists and turns. The oldest observations of superpotency for isomers of the native peptide, alpha-MSH, date to the late 1930's, and yet the drug was not officially approved until 2014 in Europe and three years later in the United States. Over the course of this long timespan, the development process stalled and was nearly terminated many times, only to be revived first in Australia and then again by a German hedge fund manager, Florian Homm. Seminal observations along the way were that prolonged exposure using the dissolving depot, greatly amplified the pigmentation effects, something that was shown first in hairless guinea pigs at the University of Arizona, and then validated in human subjects in Australia.

The chemists at Arizona, Victor Hruby and Tomi Sawyer, were the first to show that superpotency could be achieved by the exchange of the native L (levo) form of phenyalanine for the D (dextro) form of phenylalanine at position 7 in the 13-mer peptide structure of a-MSH. This substitution folded the otherwise linear peptide, a-MSH, into a U-shape with greatly enhanced binding affinity for melanocortin receptors. This seminal chemistry work was published in the late 1980's. And yet the drug development effort languished off and on for the next three decades. Such a long timeline is virtually unheard of in the terms of current drug development. In that regard, we were severely hampered by worries over carcinogenicity of a drug that has "melanocyte stimulating" in its name. We now know that far from being carcinogenic, a-MSH and its superpotent derivitives actually *reduce* the likelihood of skin cancer development, something nature was already telling us by the clear differences in skin cancer rates between fair and dark-skinned peoples. It became a case of trying to disprove a negative. That is something that can be an unending challenge to prove a drug does *not* do something deleterious.

The late Mac Hadley proved this first in northern tree frogs (*Rana Pipiens*), and then in himself! What we did not know at that time was the effects of MSH derivatives on melanocortin-4 receptors in the hypothalamus of the brain to elicit sexual arousal and later satiety (weight loss). Mac again made the seminal sexual arousal discovery with his self-injection of MT-2 and the subsequent long-lasting penile erection. Indeed, the entire Arizona story of afamelanotide development was a mosaic of different activities and different players. Chemists working with biologists and in turn with a cancer center pharmacologist and medical dermatologist. The fact that an effective drug finally emerged is a testament to both serendipity and blind disregard for the typical route of therapeutic drug development, i.e. licensing to a deep-pocketed pharma company.

There are now three melanotropin-based drugs marketed in the US by three different companies:

1. Afamelanotdie (Sceness) for the extreme light sensitivity in erythropoietic protoporphyria (EPP) patients, by Clinuvel Pharmaceuticals.
2. Bremelanotdie (Vyleesi) for hypoactive sexual desire disorder in premenopausal women, by Palatin Technologies.
3. Setmelanotide (IMCIVREE) for children 6 years of age and above with severe obesity related to proopiomelanocortin (POMC) gene mutations by Rhythm Pharmaceuticals.

Thus, what we were able to do in Arizona and Australia is initiate the discovery and commercial development of an entirely new class of drugs, *the melanocortins*. As Terry pointed out, all of this was done on extremely small amounts of capital compared to typical drug development efforts. And this is not the end of the melanocortin story. As the last chapter showed, there are many new indications being investigated for this new drug class. Indeed, the list is bewildering and includes:

1. Vitiligo
2. Inflammatory bowel disease
3. Dry eye disease
4. Arterial ischemic stroke
5. Variegate porphyria
6. Hailey-Hailey skin disease
7. Polymorphus light eruption (sun allergy)
8. Xeroderma pigmentosum-related skin cancers

And, at some point, the melanocortins may come full circle back to the truly large indication of photoprotection against skin damage and cancer in otherwise normal individuals. This was and IS the Holy Grail for this series of pigmentary peptides. Indeed, skin cancer prevention was the theme of the initial NIH Program Project Grant (PPG) that got afamelanotide into "first in human" clinical trials. Both the NIH and the FDA worked well with us to get the seminal studies completed and it remains a testament to the university system that allowed such close and pioneering collaborations to occur. The melanotropic peptide story is not shrinking. It is growing and the future holds the promise of many new discoveries and effective treatments for several conditions that currently have no effective therapies. We just wish that Mac had lived to see his drug out in the sunshine.